The James Traynor and Hugh Keevins

SPORTS QUIZ BOOK

with Alex Dowdalls

**Other books available from the
Daily Record and Sunday Mail collection:**

The Billy Sloan Rock and Pop Quiz Book

Joe Punter: At The Races

The 2002 Prize Crossword Book

The Tam Cowan Joke Book

You Are My Larsson, by Mark Guidi and Ewing Grahame

The Martin O'Neill Story, by Anna Smith and David McCarthy

**Videos available from the
Daily Record and Sunday Mail collection:**

LUBO - A Gift From God

The James Traynor and Hugh Keevins

SPORTS QUIZ BOOK

with Alex Dowdalls

First published 2001
by the Scottish Daily Record and Sunday Mail Ltd

ISBN 0-9513471-3-6

British Library Cataloguing in Publishing Data:
A catalogue record for this book is available
from the British Library.

Printed and bound in Great Britain

THIS is the sports quiz book that beats all others.
Test your knowledge against three of the best sporting
brains in the business. The accumulated knowledge of
these three Daily Record journalists ensures that this
book is much more than a series of questions...
It is a treasure trove of facts and information on just
about every sport played on this planet!

James Traynor

Scotland's leading sports journalist,
James is always in great demand as a
regular football pundit on both TV and
radio. He is rightly called Football's
Voice of Authority, thanks to his hard-
hitting articles in the Daily Record –
where he is Assistant Editor (Sport).

Hugh Keevins

Hugh joined the Daily Record sports
desk in October 2001 after four years
on the Sunday Mail, where his weekly
column sparked many a debate.
Previously with the Sunday Post and The
Scotsman, he also features as a pundit
on Radio Clyde's Superscoreboard Live.

Alex Dowdalls

A self-confessed sports fanatic, Alex
joined the Daily Record in October,
2000. Over the past 20 years he has
compiled many major sports quizzes
for both television and radio. He is an
international cricket umpire and a
former Radio Clyde broadcaster.

Tap-ins & Gimmes

EVERY golfer will tell you there's no such thing as beginner's luck... So to break you in gently, here's a selection of 250 questions that are purely for rookies.

SPL Season 2000-01

1. WHO scored four goals for Celtic in a 6-0 win over Kilmarnock on January 2, 2001?

2. AGAINST which club on April 7, 2001, did Celtic clinch the SPL title?

3. WHO scored the winning goal that wrapped up the SPL title for Celtic?

4. HENRIK Larsson was Celtic's leading scorer in the SPL with 35 goals, but who was second top with 11?

5. BY how many points did Celtic win the SPL from second-placed Rangers?

6. WHICH club was relegated from the SPL with just 30 points?

7. WHICH was the only club in the 2000-01 SPL season not to draw a game at home?

8. WHO scored five goals for Rangers against St Mirren at Ibrox in a 7-1 win on November 4, 2000?

9. WHO scored a hat-trick for Hibs in a 6-2 win over Hearts at Easter Road on October 22, 2000?

10. WHO scored hat-tricks for Aberdeen in SPL matches at home to both St Mirren and Dundee United?

ANSWERS: Turn to page 15

Bats and Balls

1. WHICH world-class off-spinner took a hat-trick for Surrey against Sussex in the 1999 Cricket County Championship?

2. FROM which country does test cricketer Nicky Boje come?

3. AMERICAN Football – Which club won the first ever Super Bowl?

4. WITH which sport would you associate the Sacramento Kings?

5. WHO was coach of the Denver Broncos from 1981 to 1992?

6. GOLF – Which Scot lost to Tiger Woods in the singles in the 1999 Ryder Cup?

7. WHICH Englishman won the 1999 Scottish PGA Open?

8. WHO did Ian Woosnam beat in the final of the 2001 Cisco World Matchplay championship at Wentworth?

9. WHICH Briton won the 1991 US Masters?

10. RUGBY League – Which side won the 2001 Rugby League Grand Final, beating Wigan at Old Trafford?

ANSWERS: Turn to page 16

The Oval Ball

1. WHICH was the first home country to lose an international against Fiji?

2. IN which country was Japan scrum-half Graeme Bachop born?

3. AGAINST which side did Scotland's Scott Murray make his international debut?

4. WHICH All Black star scored 126 points in the 1987 World Cup?

5. WHO was England's top scorer in the 1995 World Cup?

6. FOR which country does Scott Gibbs play?

7. AGAINST which nation did Scotland's Budge Poutney make his international debut in 1998?

8. WHICH international side did the father of Scotland's John Leslie captain from 1974 to 1976?

9. FROM which club did Kenny Logan join Wasps in 1996?

10. WHICH position did former Australian captain John Eales play?

ANSWERS: Turn to page 16

The Old Firm

1. HOW many players were red carded in the league game between the Old Firm on March 24, 1991?

2. WHICH Celtic player was both SPFA and Football Writers' Player of the Year in 1998?

3. WHAT was the score when Celtic beat Rangers in the 1971 Scottish Cup final replay?

4. WHAT was the score when Rangers beat Celtic in the 1973 Scottish Cup final?

5. WHICH player scored the only goal in the Celtic v Rangers 1980 Scottish Cup final?

6. WHAT did Celtic's Stevie Chalmers and Rangers' Davie Wilson achieve when they went out for the 1966-67 Scottish League Cup final?

7. WHO was the first Dutch manager to lead either of the Old Firm to league glory?

8. WHICH man, later to manage Rangers, kept goal for Berwick Rangers in 1967 when they beat Rangers 1-0 in the Scottish Cup?

9. FROM which club did Celtic sign Italian Enrico Annoni?

10. WHO, in 1966, became the first Rangers player to win the Scottish Player of the Year Award?

ANSWERS: Turn to page 17

Anyone for Tennis

1. IS Conchita Martinez right or left handed?
2. WHICH Swiss player, destined for greater things, won the girls' singles title at Wimbledon in 1994?
3. WHAT nationality is Tommy Haas?
4. WHICH country did Great Britain defeat in September 2001 to return to the World Group of the Davis Cup?

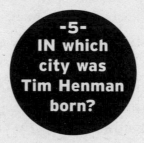

-5-
IN which city was Tim Henman born?

6. HOW many Wimbledon singles titles did Steffi Graf win from 1987 to 1999?
7. HOW many times did John McEnroe win the US Open Singles title?
8. WHEN Britain lost to the US in the 1999 Davis Cup World Group, which two players beat Greg Rusedski in the singles?
9. HOW many times did John Newcombe win the Wimbledon singles title?
10. HOW many times did Bjorn Borg win the French Open singles title?

ANSWERS: Turn to page 17

ANSWERS

SPL Season 2000-01

ANSWERS

1. Henrik Larsson;
2. St Mirren;
3. Tommy Johnson;
4. Chris Sutton;
5. 15;
6. St Mirren;
7. Rangers;
8. Kenny Miller;
9. Mixu Paatelainen;
10. Arild Stavrum.

Bats and Balls

ANSWERS

1. Saqlain Mushtaq;
2. South Africa;
3. Green Bay Packers;
4. Basketball;
5. Dan Reeves;
6. Andrew Coltart;
7. Warren Bennett;
8. Padraig Harrington;
9. Ian Woosnam;
10. Bradford Bulls.

The Oval Ball

ANSWERS

1. Scotland;
2. New Zealand;
3. Australia;
4. Grant Fox;
5. Rob Andrew;
6. Wales;
7. South Africa;
8. New Zealand;
9. Stirling County;
10. Lock.

The Old Firm

1. Four;
2. Craig Burley;
3. 2-1;
4. 3-2;
5. George McCluskey;
6. First subs to be used in a final;
7. Wim Jansen;
8. Jock Wallace;
9. A.S. Roma;
10. John Greig.

Anyone for Tennis?

1. Right;
2. Martina Hingis;
3. German;
4. Ecuador;
5. Oxford;
6. Seven;
7. Four;
8. Todd Martin and Jim Courier;
9. Three;
10. Six.

It's Just Not Cricket

1. WHO was the chicken farmer who took a hat-trick for Zimbabwe against England?

2. ON which West Indies island would you find the Kensington Oval?

-3-
FOR which county does England's Graham Thorpe play?

4. WHICH English test ground would you be at if you were sitting in the Harris Gardens?

5. IN which country was Somerset and England fast bowler Andy Caddick born?

6. WHO took 11 wickets for South Africa against England in the first test in 1999?

7. WHICH two test-playing countries play each other for the Wisden Trophy?

8. WHICH Australian test player captained Middlesex in 2000?

9. WHICH Middlesex and England bowler was awarded the MBE in 1999?

10. FOR which county does England star Darren Gough play?

ANSWERS: Turn to page 23

18

On Yer Bike

1. WHAT does TT stand for in the Isle of Man motorcycle races?

2. WHAT is another name for the sport of motocross?

3. HOW long, in miles, is the cycle ride in the triathlon Iron Man competition?

4. WHICH Scot won the 1995 individual pursuit world cycling title?

5. WHICH American finished runner-up in the 1999 World Superbike championship?

6. WHICH Briton retired in 2001 after having won four World Superbike titles?

7. WHAT nationality is top cyclist Jaan Kirsipuu?

8. WHICH country does Jan Ulrich represent in cycling?

9. WHO finished third in the 1999 World Superbike championship?

10. WHICH German, who rode club speedway in Scotland, won the 1983 world speedway championship?

ANSWERS: Turn to page 24

Fight Night

1. WHO did George Foreman beat in November 1994 in a world heavyweight title fight?

2. WHO did Evander Holyfield knock out in 1990 to become undisputed heavyweight champion?

3. AT what weight was Sugar Ray Leonard 1976 Olympic champion?

4. IN which year was Lennox Lewis born?

5. WHO did Johnny Nelson beat to take the WBO cruiserweight title in March 1999?

6. WHO beat Jersey Joe Walcott in Chicago to win the world heavyweight title in 1953?

7. AT what weight was Paul Ingle IBF champion in 2000?

8. WHO did Frank Bruno beat in September 1995 in a world heavyweight title fight?

9. IN what weight division in 1984 did Evander Holyfield win Olympic bronze?

10. WHICH legendary amateur first became world amateur heavyweight champion in 1986?

ANSWERS: Turn to page 24

Football: World Cup (1)

1. WHICH goalkeeper captained his country to World Cup glory in 1982?

2. WHO scored five goals for Russia in a 6-1 win over Cameroon in a World Cup finals match in 1994?

3. WHICH Dutchman scored the 1,000th goal in World Cup finals – against Scotland in 1978?

4. WHICH player scored for Brazil in every match of the 1970 World Cup finals?

5. WHICH country beat El Salvador 10-1 in a World Cup finals match in 1982?

6. WHICH Englishman scored against France after just 27 seconds in 1982?

7. WHICH man became the first to play and then manage a side to World Cup victory?

8. WHICH player played for Hungary in the 1954 World Cup finals and then for Spain in the 1962 finals?

9. WHICH was the first black African country to reach the World Cup finals?

10. WHICH Scotland manager resigned after Scotland's opening defeat by Austria in the 1954 finals?

ANSWERS: Turn to page 25

Life in the Fast Lane

1. WHICH Briton won bronze in the 100 metres at the 1999 World Athletics Championships?

2. WHO was declared winner of the men's 100 metres at the 1988 Olympics after Ben Johnson was stripped of the gold medal?

3. WHO was captain of the Great Britain athletics team until his retirement in 1997?

4. WHICH American won gold in both the 100 and 200 metres finals at the 1999 World Athletics Championships?

5. WHICH Brit won gold in the 110 metres hurdles at the 1999 World Athletics Championships?

6. WHO eventually broke Tommie Smith's 200 metres world record after it had stood for 11 years?

7. IN the 1972 Olympics, Renate Stecher won both the 100 and 200 metres. In each case the reigning Commonwealth Games champion followed her home for silver. Who was she?

8. WHICH British athlete won the bronze medal in the 1984 Olympic men's marathon?

9. WHO won the men's Olympic sprint double in 1976?

10. WHO won both the 100 and 200 metres men's gold medals at the 1984 Olympic games in Los Angeles?

ANSWERS: Turn to page 25

ANSWERS

It's Just Not Cricket

ANSWERS

1. Eddo Brandes;
2. Barbados;
3. Surrey;
4. Lord's;
5. New Zealand;
6. Allan Donald;
7. England and West Indies;
8. Justin Langer;
9. Angus Fraser;
10. Yorkshire.

On Yer Bike

1. Transatlantic Trophy;
2. Scrambling;
3. 112 miles;
4. Graham Obree;
5. Colin Edwards;
6. Carl Foggarty;
7. Estonian;
8. Germany;
9. Troy Corser;
10. Egon Muller.

Fight Night

1. Michael Moorer;
2. James Buster Douglas;
3. Light welterweight;
4. 1965;
5. Carl Thompson;
6. Rocky Marciano;
7. Featherweight;
8. Oliver McCall;
9. Light heavyweight;
10. Felix Savon.

Football: The World Cup

1. Dino Zoff;
2. Oleg Salenko;
3. Rob Rensenbrink;
4. Jairzinho;
5. Hungary;
6. Brian Robson;
7. Mario Zagalo;
8. Ferenc Puskas;
9. Zaire in 1974;
10. Andy Beattie.

Life in the Fast Lane

ANSWERS

1. Dwain Chambers;
2. Carl Lewis;
3. Linford Christie;
4. Maurice Greene;
5. Colin Jackson;
6. Pietro Mennea;
7. Raelene Boyle of Australia;
8. Charlie Spedding;
9. Valery Borzov;
10. Carl Lewis.

The Olympic Games

1. WHICH Brit won back-to-back gold medals in the men's 1,500 metres at the 1980 and 1984 Summer Games?

2. WHICH British woman struck gold in the javelin at the 1984 Games in Los Angeles?

3. WHICH country won the men's basketball gold at every Olympics from 1936 to 1968 inclusive?

4. WHAT was the full name of Flo Jo, the women's 100 and 200 metres gold medallist in Seoul in 1988?

5. WHICH German swimmer, who won the 100 metres butterfly at the 1984 Games, was nicknamed The Albatross?

6. WHICH Brit won gold in the women's 400 metres hurdles at the 1992 Games in Barcelona?

7. WHO was Britain's prolific goalscorer in the men's hockey team that won gold in Seoul in 1988?

8. WHICH British swimmer won the men's 100 metres breaststroke at the 1988 Olympics?

9. WHICH woman represented Britain in the 1988 Olympic women's long jump before striking gold for Italy at the same event eight years later?

10. WHICH Scot won Olympic silver in the women's 10,000 metres in 1988?

ANSWERS: Turn to page 31

The CIS Cup 2000-01

1. WHO scored a hat-trick for Celtic in their 3-0 CIS Cup final win over Kilmarnock?

2. WHO did Kilmarnock beat 3-0 in the semi-final of the CIS Cup?

3. WHICH player was sent off in the final of the CIS Cup?

4. WHO refereed last season's final?

5. WHO scored a hat-trick for Dundee United in a second round 3-0 win over Alloa Athletic?

6. WHICH First Division side did Dundee United beat 4-3 on penalties after a 0-0 draw in the third round of the competition?

7. WHO scored for Rangers in their 3-1 defeat by Celtic in the semi-final at Hampden?

8. WHO scored both goals for Hearts in their 5-2 defeat by Celtic in the quarter-final at Tynecastle?

9. WHICH First Division side did Celtic beat 4-0 at Celtic Park in the third round of the competition?

10. WHO was the first member of Celtic's CIS Cup winning side in 2000-01 to leave the club?

ANSWERS: Turn to page 32

In at the Deep End

1. WHICH Englishman won gold in the 100 metres breaststroke at the 1982 Commonwealth Games?

2. WHICH race takes place on the River Thames but in the opposite direction from the University Boat Race?

3. WHO was the diver who won medals in both platform and springboard at the Mexico Olympics in 1968?

4. ONLY one Australian swimmer won a gold medal at the Los Angeles Olympics in 1984. Who?

5. WHICH Canadian broke Scot David Wilkie's long-standing world 200 metres breaststroke record in the 1982 World Championships in Ecuador?

6. WHICH Australian girl collected three individual gold medals in the 1972 Olympic Games?

7. NEIL Cochrane won a bronze medal in the 1984 Olympics. In which event?

8. IN which event did Britain's Duncan Goodhew win an individual gold medal in the 1980 Olympics?

9. WHICH swimmer beat David Wilkie into second place in the 1972 Olympic 200 metres breaststroke, but finished behind him four years later in Montreal?

10. WHICH Scottish Olympic diver went on to become chairman of the Scottish Sports Council?

ANSWERS: Turn to page 32

Sport at the Movies

WITH which sport would you associate the following films?

1. White Men Can't Jump (1992)
2. Rookie of the Year (1993)
3. Heaven Can Wait (1978)
4. The Hustler (1961)
5. The Lemon Drop Kid (1934)
6. Bull Durham (1988)
7. Kingpin (1996)
8. Sudden Death (1995)
9. Race for Life (1954)
10. The Goalkeeper's Fear of the Penalty (1971)

ANSWERS: Turn to page 33

Sporting Terms

1. WHAT objects are released from a high house and a low house?

2. FOR which golf club is a brassie an old term?

3. IN which sport are the Eastern, Continental and Western techniques common terms?

4. WHO might use an Aberdeen, a Humpshank, a Limerick or an O'Shaughnessy?

5. IN what sport must the judge "read the phrase"?

6. TO the angler, what is a "hairy mary"?

7. WHAT is the literal meaning of the word gymnasium?

8. IN rugby union, how did the term Garryowen originate?

9. WHAT is the name given to a runner's training where he or she alternates between jogging and sprinting?

10. IN which sport would you try to knock rocks out of the house?

ANSWERS: Turn to page 33

ANSWERS

The Olympic Games

ANSWERS

1. Seb Coe;
2. Tessa Sanderson;
3. USA;
4. Florence Griffiths-Joyner;
5. Michael Gross;
6. Sally Gunnell;
7. Sean Kerly;
8. Adrian Moorehouse;
9. Fiona May;
10. Liz McColgan.

The CIS Cup 2000-01

ANSWERS

1. Henrik Larsson;
2. St Mirren;
3. Chris Sutton;
4. Hugh Dallas;
5. Stephen McConalogue;
6. Airdrie;
7. Jorg Albertz, penalty;
8. Colin Cameron;
9. Raith Rovers;
10. Ramon Vega.

In at the Deep End

ANSWERS

1. Adrian Moorehouse;
2. Head of the River Race;
3. Klaus Dibiasi;
4. John Sieben;
5. Victor Davis;
6. Shane Gould;
7. 200 metres medley;
8. 100 metres breaststroke;
9. John Hencken;
10. Peter Heatley.

Sport at the Movies

1. Basketball;
2. Baseball;
3. American Football;
4. Pool;
5. Horse Racing;
6. Baseball;
7. Ten-pin bowling;
8. Ice Hockey;
9. Motor Racing;
10. Football.

Sporting Terms

1. Clay pigeons;
2. A two wood;
3. They are all grips of a tennis racquet;
4. A fisherman. They are types of fish hooks;
5. Fencing;
6. It is a popular salmon fly;
7. School for naked exercise;
8. From Garryowen Rugby Club, Ireland;
9. Fartlek;
10. Curling.

Scottish Cup 2000-01

1. WHO did Celtic beat 3-0 to win the Tennents Scottish Cup and clinch the domestic treble?

2. WHO refereed the final?

3. WHO scored for Dundee United in their 1-0 win over Rangers in the quarter-final at Tannadice?

4. WHO scored Celtic's only goal in their 1-0 quarter-final win over Hearts at Celtic Park?

5. WHO took Celtic to a replay after a 2-2 draw in the fourth round?

6. WHICH team were awarded a walk-over against Airdrie in the fourth round after the Lanarkshire club were unable to field a side?

7. WHICH two clubs were ordered by the SFA to replay their first-round match after one side fielded an ineligible player?

8. WHICH Second Division side did Celtic beat 4-1 away from home in the third round?

9. WHO scored for Livingston in their 1-0 fourth-round replay win away to Aberdeen?

10. WHO kept goal for Celtic in the final?

ANSWERS: Turn to page 39

Derby Daze

1. WHICH horse won the 2001 Epsom Derby?

2. WHO rode Sinndar to victory in the 2000 race?

3. WHICH horse won the 1998 race at the price of 20/1?

4. WHICH trainer, in 1979 and 1980, was the last to train successive Derby winners?

5. WHICH horse did Walter Swinburn ride to victory in 1995 to notch his third Derby victory?

6. WHO trained the ill-fated Shergar to win in 1981?

7. WHO rode the Henry Cecil-trained Oath to victory in the 1999 race?

8. WHICH horse did Alan Munro partner to victory for his only Derby win in 1991?

9. WHAT was the name of the last horse Lester Piggott rode to victory in the Derby?

10. NAME the only horse trained by Saeed bin Suroor to have won the Derby?

ANSWERS: Turn to page 40

Euro 2000

1. WHO scored the winning goal for France in their 2-1 final victory over Italy?

2. WHICH country did Italy beat 3-1 on penalties in the semi-final of the competition?

3. WHO scored a hat-trick in Holland's 6-1 triumph over Yugoslavia in the quarter-finals?

4. WHO scored the Golden Goal for France in their 2-1 win over Portugal in the semi-finals?

5. WHO scored for England in their 1-0 victory over Germany in Charleroi?

6. WHICH two countries beat England in Group A to knock them out of the tournament?

7. WHICH Scottish referee took charge of the matches between Turkey and Italy and Norway against Yugoslavia?

8. WHICH Swedish referee officiated at the Euro 2000 final?

9. WHO took over in goal for England, replacing David Seaman, in their third match in the finals?

10. NAME the substitute who scored France's opening goal in the final against Italy?

ANSWERS: Turn to page 40

The Ryder Cup

1. WHAT was the final score in the 1999 Ryder Cup?

2. IN 1999, three Europeans came into the final day's singles not having played a previous match. Jarmo Sandelin and Andrew Coltart were two, who was the other?

3. WHO was the only non-Scot to win his final day singles match in 1999?

4. WHERE will the 2002 Ryder Cup be played?

5. WHICH two players were the only ones to halve their Ryder Cup singles in 1999?

6. WHICH Brit lost his singles match to Hubert Green in 1979, his first singles defeat since playing Ryder Cup golf in 1971?

7. IN which year was the Ryder Cup first played?

8. THE biennial event, which included European players instead of just Britain and Ireland, first took place in which year?

9. WHICH Scot in the 1979 event at the Greenbrier in West Virginia won four points out of five?

10. WHICH famous golf course in Ohio hosted the 1987 Ryder Cup?

ANSWERS: Turn to page 41

Football's Hot Seat

1. WHICH coach created the Magic Magyars of the 1950s?

2. WHICH Russell has been manager of both Bristol City and Cardiff City?

3. IN 1984, Dave Bassett left Wimbledon but returned after only a few days at which club?

4. MANCHESTER City chairman Francis Lee flew to Marbella to sign which holidaymaker as his new club manager?

5. WHO took Gary Lineker to Everton in 1985?

6. WHO succeeded Kenny Dalglish as manager of Blackburn Rovers?

7. WHO returned from Turkey to become boss at Southampton?

8. EX-RANGER Terry Butcher managed which Midlands side in the 1990s?

9. WHICH club side did Terry Venables manage before taking over as boss of England?

10. WHO was manager of Motherwell before Billy Davies left the club in autumn 2001?

ANSWERS: Turn to page 41

ANSWERS

Scottish Cup 2000-01

ANSWERS

1. Hibs;
2. Kenny Clark;
3. David Hannah;
4. Henrik Larsson;
5. Dunfermline Athletic;
6. Peterhead;
7. Montrose and Arbroath;
8. Stranraer;
9. Scott Crabbe;
10. Rab Douglas.

Derby Daze

1. Galileo;
2. Johnny Murtagh;
3. High-Rise;
4. Major Dick Hern;
5. Lammtarra;
6. Sir Michael Stoute;
7. Kieren Fallon;
8. Generous;
9. Teenoso;
10. Lammtarra.

Euro 2000

ANSWERS

1. David Trezeguet;
2. Holland;
3. Patrick Kluivert;
4. Zinedine Zidane;
5. Alan Shearer;
6. Romania and Portugal;
7. Hugh Dallas;
8. Anders Frisk;
9. Nigel Martyn;
10. Silvain Wiltord.

The Ryder Cup

1. USA 14, Europe 13;
2. Jean van de Velde;
3. Padraig Harrington;
4. The Belfry;
5. Justin Leonard and Jose Maria Olazabal;
6. Peter Oosterhuis;
7. 1927;
8. 1979;
9. Bernard Gallacher;
10. Muirfield Village.

Football's Hot Seat

1. Gusztav Sebes;
2. Osman;
3. Crystal Palace;
4. Alan Ball;
5. Howard Kendall;
6. Ray Harford;
7. Graeme Souness;
8. Coventry City;
9. Tottenham Hotspur;
10. Harri Kampman.

Speedway

1. WHO won the 2001 Speedway World Championship for the fourth time?

2. WHICH famous speedway club are nicknamed the Aces?

3. BEFORE moving to Ashfield, where did the Glasgow Tigers ride?

4. FROM which country does world speedway star Tomaz Gollob hail from?

5. AT which stadium did the Monarchs ride when they were based in Coatbridge?

6. WHICH English speedway team are nicknamed the Diamonds?

7. IVAN Mauger and Barry Briggs were both stars from which country?

8. WHICH stadium hosted the 2001 British leg of the Speedway World Championship Grand Prix?

9. IN a league match, what are the traditional helmet colours for the two home riders?

10. FROM which country does speedway star Sam Ermolenko come?

ANSWERS: Turn to page 47

Be a Devil

1. WHO were Manchester United's opponents in the 1968 European Cup final?

2. WHICH ex-Manchester United player became Jack Charlton's assistant with the Republic of Ireland?

3. ERIC Cantona scored for United in his comeback in October 1995, but against which club?

4. WHO came after Dave Sexton as boss at Old Trafford in 1981?

5. WHO succeeded Sir Matt Busby as the manager of Man U?

6. WHO scored from the penalty spot for United in the 1980 FA Cup final replay?

7. WHO was Martin Buchan's brother – also a professional footballer?

8. WHO was sent off in Manchester United's 1990's European champions league 3-1 defeat in Gothenburg?

9. RAY Wilkins moved from Manchester United to which club for £1.5 million in June, 1984?

10. WHICH Old Trafford legend scored 49 goals for England?

ANSWERS: Turn to page 48

Hail, Hail

1. WHO is Martin O'Neill's assistant manager at Celtic?

2. UP to and including the 2000-01 season, how many times have Celtic been crowned league champions?

3. HENRIK Larsson was Celtic's leading scorer in the Tennents Scottish Cup last season with nine goals, but who was second with three?

4. WHO managed Celtic immediately prior to Tommy Burns?

5. WHO, with 80 appearances for his country, is Celtic's most capped player?

6. CELTIC have won the League Cup for the last two seasons. But prior to that, when was the last time they won the trophy two years in a row?

7. HOW many league games did Henrik Larsson miss for Celtic during the 2000-01 season?

8. WHO is Celtic's head youth coach?

9. WHO scored Celtic's first league goal of last season 2000-01?

10. WHO scored Celtic's last league goal of last season 2000-01?

ANSWERS: Turn to page 48

Follow, Follow

1. WHO, with 11 goals, was Rangers' leading league goalscorer last season, 2000-01?

2. HOW many times have Rangers won the league title?

3. WHO, with 60 caps, is Rangers' most capped player?

4. FOR which player have Rangers received their biggest ever transfer fee?

5. APART from Dick Advocaat, how many different managers have Rangers had since 1975?

6. WHICH Dutchman is Gers' first-team coach under Dick Advocaat?

7. WHO, with 44 goals, holds the record for the most numbers of goals for Rangers in any one season?

8. AGAINST which club did Rangers chalk up their biggest league win in season 2000-01?

9. WHO scored Rangers' first goal in season 2000-01?

10. WHO scored Rangers' last goal of season 2000-01?

ANSWERS: Turn to page 49

Strawberries and Cream

1.   WHICH player appeared in Wimbledon's men's singles finals at the age of 19 and 39?

2.   WHICH brothers asked to wear England shirts while playing at Wimbledon during football's Euro 96?

3.   WHO was the first woman to be elected to the Wimbledon championship committee?

4.   WHO was the first male Brit to win a Wimbledon title after Fred Perry?

5.   WHO was the last men's singles champion at Wimbledon before it went open?

6.   WHO did Chris Evert beat to win her first Wimbledon singles title?

7.   HOW many times did Martina Navratilova win the women's singles at Wimbledon as a Czech?

> **8. HOW many times did Czech Ivan Lendl win Wimbledon?**

9.   WITH whom did Ann Jones win the Wimbledon mixed doubles title in 1969?

10.   WHOSE match had been interrupted by rain when Cliff Richard staged an impromptu concert on Centre Court?

ANSWERS: Turn to page 49

ANSWERS

Speedway

ANSWERS

1. Tony Rickardsson;
2. Belle Vue;
3. Shawfield Stadium;
4. Poland;
5. Cliftonhill Stadium;
6. Newcastle;
7. New Zealand;
8. The Millennium Stadium, Cardiff;
9. Red and Blue;
10. USA.

Be a Devil

ANSWERS

1. Benfica;
2. Maurice Setters;
3. Liverpool;
4. Ron Atkinson;
5. Wilf McGuinness;
6. Arnold Muhren;
7. George;
8. Paul Ince;
9. A.C. Milan;
10. Bobby Charlton.

Hail, Hail

ANSWERS

1. John Robertson;
2. 37;
3. Jackie McNamara;
4. Lou Macari;
5. Paddy Bonner;
6. 1968-69 and 1969-70;
7. One, the last against Kilmarnock;
8. Willie McStay;
9. Henrik Larsson (v Dundee United);
10. Lubo Moravcik (v Hibs).

Follow, Follow

1. Tore Andre Flo;
2. 49 times;
3. Ally McCoist;
4. Trevor Steven;
5. Four;
6. Jan Wouters;
7. Sam English;
8. St Mirren 7-1;
9. Billy Dodds (v St Johnstone);
10. Tony Vidmar (v Hibs).

Strawberries and Cream

1. Ken Rosewall;
2. Luke and Murphy Jensen;
3. Virginia Wade;
4. John Lloyd;
5. John Newcombe;
6. Olga Morozova;
7. Twice;
8. None;
9. Fred Stolle;
10. Pete Sampras and Richard Krajicek.

Goal-den opportunity

YOU'VE only got the keeper to beat in this selection of teasers... so will it be the applause of the fans or a howler worthy of A Question of Sport's 'What Happened Next?' Fingers on the buzzer...

51

English Premiership
2000-01

1. WHO played his 500th game for Manchester United in the Premiership match against Liverpool on March 17, 2001?

2. WHO was Manchester United's leading league scorer last season with 15 goals?

3. WHO scored a hat-trick for Manchester United in their 6-1 win over Arsenal at Old Trafford on February 25, 2001?

4. WHO had the best home league record in the Premiership – losing just one game in front of their own fans all season?

5. WHO won both the PFA and the English Football Writers' Player of the Year awards?

6. WHO was named Carling Manager of the Year?

7. WHO teamed up with Brian Robson in management at Middlesbrough in December, 2000 after they went bottom of the Premiership?

8. WHO was Arsenal's leading league scorer with 17 goals?

9. HOW many league games did Andy Goram play for Manchester United?

10. AGAINST which club did Goram make his league debut for the champions?

ANSWERS: Turn to page 57

Scots Golfing Heroes

1. WHICH Scot was vice-captain at the 1999 Ryder Cup?

2. WHICH fellow Scot beat Sandy Lyle to win the British Boys' Championship and followed up with victories in the Scottish Boys' and the British Youths' championships?

3. WHICH Scot was awarded the MBE in the 1987 New Year's Honours list?

4. WHICH Scot, who has never won a major, led both the 1979 and 1984 British Opens after the first round?

5. FROM which town in Scotland does Bernard Gallacher come?

6. WHICH Scot, now a well-known commentator, won the Dutch Open in 1983 and the Glasgow Open in 1984?

7. WHICH Scot was European Tour Rookie of the Year in 1982?

8. NAME the Scot who won the Carrolls Irish Open in 1981 having won the Australian PGA Championship the previous year?

9. FOUR Scots were in the 1979 Ryder Cup team – Sandy Lyle, Bernard Gallacher, Ken Brown and who else?

10. WHICH Scot became the first European to win the European Open in 1979?

ANSWERS: Turn to page 58

Horses for Courses

1. IN which month each year is Royal Ascot traditionally held?

2. IN 1990 Mr Frisk set a record time in which major race?

3. WHERE is the Lincoln handicap run?

-4-
WHICH three races make up the English triple crown?

5. HOW long is the Derby?

6. HOW old was Lester Piggott when he returned to racing in 1990?

7. RIDING Erhaab in 1994, which jockey won his fourth Epsom Derby?

8. WHICH horse was National Hunt Champion of the Year four times in a row from 1987?

9. WHO triumphed in the Oaks on Ballanchine and Moonshell?

10. HOW many times did Sir Gordon Richards win the Epsom Derby?

ANSWERS: Turn to page 58

The Grand Nationals

1. WHO rode Grittar to victory in the 1982 Grand National?

2. RED Rum came second in the National twice. Who were the horses that beat him?

3. IN which year did Bob Champion ride Aldaniti to victory in the Grand National?

4. OVER which course is the Scottish Grand National run?

5. WHEN Golden Miller set a record time for the Grand National in 1934 it stood for years. Who eventually beat it?

6. ON which course is the Welsh Grand National run?

7. TOMMY Carberry won the Irish Grand National two years running on the same horse. Which one?

8. OVER which Liverpool course is the Grand National held each year?

9. HOW many fences are jumped on the Liverpool course?

10. WHICH horse won the 1968 Grand National?

ANSWERS: Turn to page 59

Scots clubs in Europe
2000-01

1. WHICH Irish club knocked Aberdeen out of the UEFA Cup in the qualifying round?

2. WHICH side from Luxembourg did Celtic beat in the qualifying round of the UEFA Cup?

3. WHICH club knocked Celtic out of the UEFA Cup, beating Martin O'Neill's side 3-2 on aggregate?

4. WHICH side knocked Hearts out of the UEFA Cup in the first round on the away goals rule?

5. WHICH German side sent Rangers out of the UEFA Cup 3-1 on aggregate in the third round?

6. WHICH club did Rangers beat 5-0 in the opening Champions League match on September 12, 2000?

7. WHO scored Rangers' winning goal in their 1-0 win in Monaco in the Champions League section match?

8. WHO replaced Stefan Klos in goal for Rangers for their last two Champions League matches?

9. WHO did Rangers beat in the second qualifying round to eventually win through to the Champions League?

10. WHO scored a hat-trick for Celtic in the UEFA Cup?

ANSWERS: *Turn to page 59*

ANSWERS

English Premiership 2000-01

ANSWERS

1. Dennis Irwin;
2. Teddy Sheringham;
3. Dwight Yorke;
4. Arsenal;
5. Teddy Sheringham;
6. George Burley of Ipswich Town;
7. Terry Venables;
8. Thierry Henry;
9. Two;
10. Coventry City.

Scots Golfing Heroes

ANSWERS

1.   Sam Torrance;
2.   Brian Marchbank;
3.   Sandy Lyle;
4.   Bill Longmuir;
5.   Bathgate;
6.   Ken Brown;
7.   Gordon Brand Junior;
8.   Sam Torrance;
9.   Brian Barnes;
10.   Sandy Lyle.

Horses for Courses

ANSWERS

1.   June;
2.   Grand National;
3.   Doncaster;
4.   2000 Guineas, Derby and St Leger;
5.   One mile and four furlongs;
6.   54;
7.   Willie Carson;
8.   Desert Orchid;
9.   Frankie Dettori;
10.   Once.

The Grand Nationals

1.   Dick Saunders;
2.   L' Escargot and Rag Trade;
3.   1981;
4.   Ayr;
5.   Red Rum;
6.   Chepstow;
7.   Brown Lad;
8.   Aintree;
9.   30;
10.   Red Alligator.

Scots clubs in Europe 2000-01

1.   Bohemians;
2.   Jeunesse Esch;
3.   Bordeaux;
4.   Stuttgart;
5.   Kaiserslautern;
6.   Sturm Graz;
7.   Giovanni van Bronckhorst;
8.   Jens Christiansen;
9.   Zalgiris Kaunas;
10.   Mark Burchill against Jeunesse Esch.

Women in Sport

1. IN what sport did Britain's Jane Bridge win a world title?

2. WHO is the sporting sister of showjumper David Broome?

3. NAME the two Swiss skiers who took gold and silver medals in the 1984 Olympic women's downhill?

4. AT what sport did Mary Lou Retton and Ecaterina Szabo excel?

5. WHICH British swimmer won the gold medal in the women's 200 metres breaststroke at the 1960 Rome Olympics?

6. WHO was selected as Female Athlete of the Year in Britain in 1980?

7. OF which gymnast was it said "she never cried"?

8. WHICH French tennis player lost in six Wimbledon doubles finals between 1965 and 1975?

9. WITH which sport would you associate Allison Fisher?

10. WHICH British long jumper won gold at the 1964 Olympics in Tokyo?

ANSWERS: Turn to page 65

What a Year - 1988

1. KAHYASI won the Epsom Derby, but who was the jockey?

2. WHO won the women's singles Olympic Games gold medal in tennis – the first time the sport had been back in the Games since 1924?

3. WHO won both the men's platform and springboard diving gold medals at the Olympics?

4. WHICH legendary Danish rider won the World speedway championship?

5. WHICH Argentinian did Steffi Graf partner to win the women's doubles at Wimbledon?

6. WHICH skiier won both the slalom and giant slalom at the Winter Olympics?

7. WHO won the British Open golf championship at Royal Lytham?

8. WHO won the US Open golf championship, six shots ahead of second placed Jeff Sluman?

9. WHICH legendary boxer beat Donny Lalonde to win the WBC light heavyweight and WBC super middleweight titles?

10. WHO won both the men's 100 metres and the long jump at the Olympics?

ANSWERS: Turn to page 66

FA Cup 2000-01

1. LIVERPOOL beat Arsenal 2-1 in the final but who scored both goals for the Merseyside club?

2. WHO scored Arsenal's goal?

3. WHO did Arsenal beat 2-1 in the semi-final?

4. WHICH non-league club lost 1-0 to Bristol City in a fourth-round replay?

5. WHICH fellow London club did Arsenal beat 6-0 in the fourth round?

6. WHICH club knocked out Manchester United, beating them 1-0 at Old Trafford?

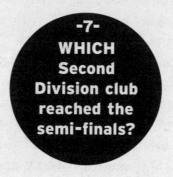

-7-
WHICH
Second
Division club
reached the
semi-finals?

8. WHO scored the winning goal to knock out Manchester United?

9. WHICH non-league side took Premiership Charlton to a replay in the third round?

10. WHERE was the Cup final played?

ANSWERS: Turn to page 66

Kings of the Ring

1. IN 1997, Mike Tyson was disqualified for biting the ear of which opponent?

2. IN April 1985, Marvin Hagler beat a man who had previously won the welterweight and light middleweight world titles. Who was he?

3. BRITISH boxers have won four Olympic gold medals in the middleweight division. Who was the last to win one?

4. IN the World Amateur Championship, the 1978 featherweight champion won the lightweight title four years later. Who was he?

5. WHICH famous boxer, nicknamed the Manassa Mauler, died in 1983?

6. WHICH world featherweight champion was undefeated until his tragic death in 1982?

7. IN March 1980, the great Sugar Ray Leonard defended his world title successfully against which British boxer?

8. WHO did Britain's Charlie Magri beat for the world flyweight title in September 1983?

9. WHICH boxer deprived John H. Stracey of his WBC world welterweight crown at Wembley in June 1976?

10. WHICH world heavyweight champion retired in 1956 having never lost a professional fight?

ANSWERS: Turn to page 67

Champions League 2000-01

1. WHO won the 2000/01 European Champions league?

2. WHERE was the final played?

3. WHICH Dutchman refereed the final?

4. THE final was decided on penalties after a 1-1 draw. Name the two scorers in normal time?

5. WHICH English club lost in the semi-final?

6. WHICH club knocked Arsenal out at the quarter-final stage?

7. WHICH was the only club unbeaten in the first Group stages?

8. RANGERS failed to qualify from the first stage, finishing third in Group D, but which club won their Group?

9. WHICH Portuguese side failed to win a single match in the first stage?

10. MANCHESTER United lost 2-1 in the quarter-final second leg to Bayern Munich, but who scored for United in the Olympic Stadium?

ANSWERS: Turn to page 67

ANSWERS

Women in Sport

ANSWERS

1. Judo;
2. Liz Edgar;
3. Michela Figini and Maria Walliser;
4. Gymnastics;
5. Anita Lonsborough;
6. Kathy Smallwood (now Cook);
7. Nadia Comanechi;
8. Francoise Durr;
9. Snooker;
10. Mary Rand.

What a Year - 1988

1. Ray Cochrane;
2. Steffi Graf;
3. Greg Louganis;
4. Hans Neilsen;
5. Gabriella Sabatini;
6. Alberto Tomba;
7. Seve Ballesteros;
8. Curtis Strange;
9. Sugar Ray Leonard;
10. Carl Lewis.

FA Cup 2000-01

1. Michael Owen;
2. Freddy Ljunberg;
3. Wycombe Wanderers;
4. Spurs;
5. Kingstonian;
6. QPR;
7. West Ham United;
8. Paolo di Canio;
9. Dagenham and Redbridge;
10. The Millennium Stadium, Cardiff.

Kings of the Ring

ANSWERS

1.   Evander Holyfield;
2.   Thomas Hearns;
3.   Chris Finnegan (1968);
4.   Angel Herrera (Cuba);
5.   Jack Dempsey;
6.   Wilfred Benitez;
7.   Dave Boy Green;
8.   Frank Cedeno;
9.   Carlos Palomino;
10.   Rocky Marciano.

Champions League 2000-01

ANSWERS

1.   Bayern Munich;
2.   San Siro, Milan;
3.   Dick Jol;
4.   Effenberg and Mendieta;
5.   Leeds United;
6.   Valencia;
7.   Deportivo La Coruna;
8.   Sturm Graz;
9.   Sporting Lisbon;
10.   Ryan Giggs.

Don't be Snookered

1. WHO did Stephen Hendry whitewash 5-0 in the third round of the Regal Masters Scottish Open in 2000?

2. WHICH South African player did Dennis Taylor beat in the first round of the 1975 Embassy World Professional Championship?

3. A TOTAL clearance taking the yellow ball after each red would result in what break?

4. IN which Scottish town does snooker star Marco Fu now stay?

5. WHICH Welshman knocked John Higgins out of the 1999 Liverpool Victoria UK Championship in the semi-finals?

6. WHO headed the world rankings from 1990 to 1998?

7. WHICH Welshman won the 1980 Benson and Hedges Masters?

8. NAME the Englishman who won the 1992 European Open?

9. WHO beat Mark Williams in the final of the 2000 Regal Scottish Open?

10. WHICH South African won the 1985 British Open?

ANSWERS: Turn to page 73

In What Sport?

1.   LUTZ is a term used in which sport?

2.   ESKIMO Roll is a term used in which sport?

3.   IN athletics, what is a Fosbury Flop?

4.   JIB, Halyards and Sheets are terms used in which sport?

5.   IN which sport would you use the term dormie?

6.   THE term face-off is used in which sport?

7.   WITH which sport would you associate John and Michael Whittaker?

-8-
WITH which sport would you associate Maureen Flowers?

9.   IF you were trying to put a rock in the house which sport would you be playing?

10. WHICH sport would you be watching if the Salford Reds were playing the Bradford Bulls?

ANSWERS: Turn to page 74

Martial Arts

1. WHAT is the highest grade awarded in judo?

2. WHICH country won eight gold medals at the 1999 World Judo Championship?

3. SCOT David Murphy, from Lanarkshire, is a three times world champion in which martial art?

4. WHICH British judo player won a bronze in the open category in the Moscow Olympics of 1980?

5. JUDO expert Ernesto Perez comes from which country?

6. WHICH British Judo player retired after the 1972 Olympics with two gold medals and two world titles?

7. WHO, by winning the middleweight category in 1970, became the first Briton to take gold in the European championships?

8. IF a judo exponent describes himself as a ninth Dan, what colour of belt does he wear?

9. WHAT is the name for a full point and victory in judo?

10. WHICH two Britons won judo bronze medals at the Los Angeles Olympics in 1984?

ANSWERS: Turn to page 74

Mixed Bag (1)

1. WHAT is the club song of West Ham United?

2. WHICH sport was named after the home of the Duke of Beaufort?

3. WHAT is the diameter in metres of the circle from which a discus is thrown?

4. WHICH two Danish badminton players won All England men's singles titles during the 1970s?

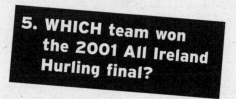

5. WHICH team won the 2001 All Ireland Hurling final?

6. HOW many players are there in each side of an Australian Rules football team?

7. IN which Olympic Games were women's athletics events included for the first time?

8. IN which year was the first London Marathon held?

9. IN athletics, how many events are there in the heptathlon?

10. WHAT is the name of the rubber disc used in ice hockey?

ANSWERS: Turn to page 75

True or False

1. THERE are 21 balls on the table at the start of a game of snooker.
2. LOURDES Dominguez is a professional tennis player.
3. LANDRY Zahana-Oni played for Stirling Albion in 1997.
4. GAY Kelleway rode Bula to victory in the 1971 and 1972 Champion Hurdle?

5. ELEVEN Wise FC were football champions of Ghana in 1960?

6. BOXER Mike Tyson has addressed the Oxford Union on the subject of The History of the American Indian?
7. FORMER US President George Bush Snr won an Olympic bronze medal in 1952 for Clay Pigeon shooting.
8. PEGGY Beer is a German heptathlete?
9. BAD Lye is a golf course in Germany.
10. INVINCIBLE Eleven are former football league champions of Liberia.

ANSWERS: Turn to page 75

ANSWERS

Don't be Snookered

ANSWERS

1. Lee Walker;
2. Perrie Mans;
3. 72;
4. Stirling;
5. Matthew Stevens;
6. Stephen Hendry;
7. Terry Griffiths;
8. Jimmy White;
9. Ronnie O'Sullivan;
10. Silvino Francisco.

In What Sport?

1. Ice skating;
2. Canoeing;
3. A type of high jump;
4. Sailing;
5. Golf;
6. Ice hockey;
7. Showjumping;
8. Darts;
9. Curling;
10. Rugby league.

Martial Arts

1. 12th Dan white belt;
2. Japan;
3. Tae Kwon do;
4. Arthur Mapp;
5. Spain;
6. Dave Starbrook;
7. Brian Jacks;
8. Red;
9. Ippon;
10. Neil Eckersley and Kerrith Brown.

Mixed Bag (1)

ANSWERS

1. I'm Forever Blowing Bubbles;
2. Badminton;
3. 2.5 metres;
4. Svend Pri (1975); and
   Flemming Delfs (1977);
5. Tipperary;
6. 18;
7. 1928;
8. 1981;
9. Seven;
10. A puck.

True or False

ANSWERS

1. False;
2. True;
3. True;
4. False;
5. True;
6. False;
7. False;
8. True;
9. False;
10. True.

Figure it Out

ALL the answers in this round are a number.

1. HOW many caps did Gordon Banks win for England? Was it 43, 53, or 73?

2. HOW many goals did both Bobby Charlton and Gary Lineker each score for England?

3. HOW many caps did Paul McStay win for Scotland? Was it 66, 70 or 76?

4. HOW many of Celtic's 19 home Premier League games in 2000-01 did they win, 17, 18 or 19?

5. HOW many home league games did Montrose win in season 2000-01 in the Third Division? Was it one, two or three?

6. HOW many goals overall did Ally McCoist score for Rangers? Was it 305, 325 or 355?

7. HOW many appearances in his career did goalkeeper Alan Ball make for Queen of the South? Was it 631, 731 or 831?

8. HOW many times have Aberdeen appeared in the European Cup – once, twice or three times?

9. HOW many goals were scored in the 2001 UEFA Cup Final?

10. WILLIE Henderson of Rangers won 29, 30 or 31 full international caps?

ANSWERS: Turn to page 81

Car Crazy

1. IN motor racing, what does the yellow flag signify?

2. IN what year did Nigel Mansell win the Formula One World motor racing championship?

3. WHERE was the first motor racing Grand Prix held in 1906?

4. ENGLAND'S Richard Burns was beaten by seven points for the 1999 World Rally Championship by which Finnish driver?

5. AUSTRALIA'S Alan Jones won the Formula One championship in 1980, but who before him was the last Australian to win the title?

6. WHICH New Zealand driver won the World Formula One title in 1967?

7. WHICH Frenchman failed to win the World Formula One championship in 1983 despite having four Grand Prix victories that season?

8. WHICH British driver raced in 90 consecutive Grand Prix races in the 1960s

9. WHICH driver won the 1985 Portuguese Grand Prix – the first of his career – and in doing so lapped all but one of the field?

10. WHICH British driver was runner-up in the 2001 Formula One championship?

ANSWERS: Turn to page 82

Behind the Mike

1. AT which Formula One circuit did Murray Walker commentate on his last Grand Prix?

2. WHICH famous ITV football commentator died in September 2001?

3. WITH which sport do you associate the commentator Andy Jameson?

4. COMMENTATOR Dave Lanning is famous for covering two sports – darts is one but what is the other?

5. WITH which sport would you associate commentator Sid Waddell?

6. HENRY Bloefeld is a commentator on which sport?

7. EDDIE Hemming and Mike "Stevo" Stephenson are commentators in which sport?

8. BRIAN Johnston and John Arlott were famous for covering which sport?

9. WHO has succeeded Murray Walker as ITV's Formula One commentator?

10. WHICH Olympic gold medallist is BBC's new top commentator for rowing?

ANSWERS: Turn to page 82

Up for the Cup

1. IN which year was the first FA Cup Final held?

2. WHAT is the name of the international biennial yachting event coinciding with Cowes Week?

-3-
THE Curtis Cup is awarded for which sport?

4. THE Wightman Cup is played for in which sport?

5. THE Westchester Cup is presented in which sport?

6. THE Cheltenham and Gloucester Cup replaced the Nat West Trophy in which sport?

7. THE Vince Lombardi Trophy is played for in which sport?

8. THE Harry Sunderland Trophy is presented to the man of the match in which sporting event?

9. THE Corbillion Cup is competed for in which sport?

10. WHAT is the proper name for the Rugby Union World Cup trophy?

ANSWERS: Turn to page 83

Name the Year

1. IN which year was the first radio cricket commentary broadcast?

2. WHEN was the UK Professional Snooker Championship inaugurated?

3. IN which year was the Cesarewitch horse race first run at Newmarket?

4. IN which year did Roy Emerson and Maria Bueno win Wimbledon?

5. IN which year did Roger Bannister break the four-minute mile barrier?

6. IN which year did the Henley Regatta first take place?

7. NAME the year in which an Australian cricket team first toured England.

8. IN which year did Rangers first win the Scottish Cup?

9. NAME the year in which Belgian Eddy Merckx first won the Tour de France.

10. IN which year did Celtic first win the Scottish League Cup?

ANSWERS: Turn to page 83

ANSWERS

Figure it Out

ANSWERS

1. 73;
2. 49;
3. 76;
4. 17;
5. One;
6. 355;
7. 731;
8. Three;
9. Nine;
10. 29.

Car Crazy

ANSWERS

1. No overtaking;
2. Mario Andretti;
3. Stirling Moss;
4. Nurembergring;
5. Jack Brabham;
6. Denny Hulme;
7. Alain Prost;
8. Graham Hill;
9. Ayrton Senna;
10. David Coulthard.

Behind the Mike

ANSWERS

1. Indianapolis;
2. Brian Moore;
3. Swimming;
4. Speedway;
5. Darts;
6. Cricket;
7. Rugby League;
8. Cricket;
9. James Allen;
10. Gary Herbert.

Up for the Cup

1.   1872;
2.   Admirals Cup;
3.   Golf;
4.   Tennis;
5.   Polo;
6.   Cricket;
7.   American Football – The Super Bowl;
8.   Rugby League Grand Final;
9.   Table Tennis;
10. The Webb Ellis Trophy.

Name the Year

1.   1922 in Australia;
2.   1977;
3.   1839;
4.   1965;
5.   1954;
6.   1839;
7.   1878;
8.   1894;
9.   1969;
10. 1956-57.

The Rugby Union World Cup 1999

1.   WHICH Englishman, with 69 points, was the top scorer of any home country team?

2.   WHO was England's top try scorer with four?

3.   WHERE was the final played?

4.   WHICH country won the Cup and who did they beat in the final?

5.   WHAT was the score in the final?

6.   NAME the beaten semi-finalists?

-7-
THE top points scorer was Argentinian. But what was his name?

8.   WHICH Australian, with 101 points, was the tournament's second-top scorer?

9.   WHICH country won the third/fourth play-off?

10.   WHICH country beat Scotland at Murrayfield in the quarter-finals?

ANSWERS: Turn to page 89

It's a Record

1. WHO was the first player to score 100 goals in the English Premiership?

2. WHO, in 1993, was the first black footballer to captain England in a full international?

3. WHO set a record 13-2 aggregate win against Fulham in the League Cup in 1986?

4. WHO, in 1968, set the world long jump record for men?

5. WHO has won the world individual speedway title the most times?

6. WHICH American swimmer set 27 individual records for freestyle and butterfly between 1967 and 1972?

7. WHICH British sportsman clinched a world title at Mount Fuji, Japan, in 1976?

8. WHO is the youngest man to have won the world squash title?

9. WHO was transferred from Barcelona to Napoli in 1984 for a then world record £5.5 million?

10. WHICH tennis player, in 1984, became the richest sportswoman in the world?

ANSWERS: Turn to page 90

Name the Nation

1. IN which country would you find the Kyalami Grand Prix circuit?

2. IN which country were the 1988 Winter Olympics held?

3. WHICH was the only Eastern bloc country not to boycott the 1984 Olympic Games in Los Angeles?

4. FROM which country does Formula One motor racing star Kimi Raikonnen come?

5. WHO did West Germany play in the 1980 European Football Championship final?

6. FROM which country does Celtic's Bobo Balde originate?

7. WHICH country does tennis star Nicola Lapenti come from?

8. WHICH country did long distance runner Miruts Yifter represent?

9. WHICH two countries will jointly host the 2002 World Cup finals?

10. BEFORE becoming a French citizen, which country did tennis star Yannick Noah come from?

ANSWERS: Turn to page 90

Sporting Trivia

1. IN 1984, which footballer, later to become England manager, declared his ambition was to ride in the Grand National?

2. WHAT flower is the emblem of Glamorgan County Cricket Club?

3. ON what day of the year does a horse have its official birthday?

4. WHO, in 1983, made an appearance at a Conservative Party rally and went on to make his debut as a television chat-show host?

5. WHO headed the England cricket team which toured the USA in 1872?

6. WHICH brother and sister pairing won the mixed doubles at Wimbledon in 1980?

7. WHAT do cricketers Ian Botham, Arnie Sidebottom and the late David Bairstow all have in common outside cricket?

8. WHO played the part of snooker ace Flash Gordon in the film Number One?

9. WHO was protected by 18 bodyguards when he visted Wimbledon in 1985?

10. WHAT is the official national sport of Canada?

ANSWERS: Turn to page 91

Scottish International Football

1. HOW many appearances did Denis Law make for his country?

2. WITH which club was Steve Archibald playing when he won the first of his 27 caps?

3. AGAINST which country did John Collins win the last of his 58 caps?

4. MANCHESTER United's Stewart Houston won his only full cap in 1976. Against whom?

5. GARY McAllister, then with Leicester City, won his first Scottish cap against East Germany – but in which year?

6. CELTIC assistant boss John Robertson won 28 caps while playing for two different clubs. Nottingham Forest was one, name the other?

7. WHAT was the venue in Glasgow in 1872 for the first match between Scotland and England?

8. WHO beat Scotland 2-0 at Hampden in 1962, the first home defeat for 25 years?

9. WHO did Scotland beat 2-0 in May 1930, their first official international abroad?

10. WHO, in March 1986, presented Kenny Dalglish with a golden cap to mark his 100th international appearance?

ANSWERS: Turn to page 91

ANSWERS

Rugby Union World Cup 1999

ANSWERS

1.   Johnny Wilkinson;
2.   Dan Luger;
3.   The Millennium Stadium, Cardiff;
4.   Australia beat France;
5.   35-12;
6.   South Africa and New Zealand;
7.   Gonzalo Quesada with 102 points;
8.   Matt Burke;
9.   South Africa;
10.   New Zealand.

It's a Record

1. Alan Shearer;
2. Paul Ince;
3. Liverpool;
4. Bob Beamon;
5. Ivan Mauger;
6. Mark Spitz;
7. James Hunt;
8. Jahangir Khan, Pakistan;
9. Diego Maradonna;
10. Martina Navratilova.

Name the Nation

ANSWERS

1. South Africa;
2. Canada;
3. Romania;
4. Finland;
5. Belgium;
6. French Guinea;
7. Ecuador;
8. Ethiopia;
9. Japan and South Korea;
10. Cameroon.

Sporting Trivia

ANSWERS

1.   Kevin Keegan;
2.   Daffodil;
3.   January 1;
4.   Steve Davis;
5.   W.G. Grace;
6.   John and Tracey Austin;
7.   They all played professional football;
8.   Bob Geldof;
9.   Frank Sinatra;
10.   Lacrosse.

Scottish International Football

ANSWERS

1.   55;
2.   Aberdeen;
3.   England;
4.   Denmark;
5.   1990;
6.   Derby County;
7.   Hamilton Crescent, Partick (West of Scotland Cricket Club);
8.   England;
9.   France;
10.   Franz Beckenbauer.

Turning on a half chance

Section Three

YOU win some, you lose some. Our questions are getting tougher – but don't be afraid to have a stab... Your answers will either burst the net or go out for a throw-in.

Equestrian

1. WHICH American won the individual gold medal for showjumping at the 1984 Olympics in Los Angeles?

2. WHICH German showjumper won the 1976 gold medal in Montreal without a single fault?

3. NAME the Scot who won both team and individual Olympic silvers in the three-day event at the 1988 Games in Seoul?

4. WHICH brothers won silver medals in the team event in the 1984 Olympic showjumping?

5. WHO, in 1968, became the first American rider to win the Queen Elizabeth II Cup?

6. WHO set a British jumping record on Lastic in 1978?

7. WHICH rider won the Queen Elizabeth II Cup four times between 1977 and 1982?

8. WHICH rider won the Hickstead Derby four times in the 1970s?

9. WHICH British rider took the individual silver medal in the 1982 showjumping World Championships?

10. WHICH famous German showjumper won the 1974 World Championship?

ANSWERS: Turn to page 99

All American Show

1. WHICH sport takes as its law "The Harvard Rules"?

2. WHICH American beat Britain's Colin Jackson to the gold in the 110 metres hurdles at the 1988 Olympics in Seoul?

3. WHICH American boxer was beaten in highly controversial circumstances for gold in the light-middleweight boxing division of the 1988 Olympics in Seoul?

4. WILLIAM Steinkraus won summer Olympic gold for the USA in 1968 in an individual event. Which one?

5. TO whom in American Football is the Heisman Trophy awarded?

6. WHICH baseball team was sold for $21 million in 1980?

7. WHO won the 1972 Olympic basketball final with a second to play?

8. WHICH National League baseball team play at Veterans Stadium?

9. WHAT is the only substance that can be applied to the baseball bat?

10. WHO, in 1969, was named the greatest ever player by the Baseball Writers' Association?

ANSWERS: Turn to page 100

Just for Keeps

1. WHICH Spanish goalkeeper was signed from Airdrie by Livingston?

2. WHICH keeper did Dunfermline Athletic recruit from Dutch side Go Ahead Eagles?

3. WHO kept goal for Tottenham Hotspur in the 1984 UEFA Cup final?

4. **WHICH keeper returned to Dundee after a spell with Linfield?**

5. WITH which club did England keeper Nigel Martyn begin his career?

6. WHAT nationality is Sunderland goalie Thomas Sorensen?

7. WHICH three French clubs did Fabien Barthez play for before joining Manchester United?

8. FROM which club did Liverpool sign Sander Westerveld?

9. WITH which club did Tim Flowers begin his senior career in 1984?

10. WHICH ex-Albion Rovers and Sheffield United keeper made one full appearance for Scotland in 1975?

ANSWERS: Turn to page 100

Strange Goals in Football

1. WHO scored after four seconds for Bradford Park Avenue against Tranmere in 1964?

2. WHO scored for Real Zaragoza against Arsenal from 40 yards out on the touchline to win the European Cup Winners' Cup in 1995?

3. WHICH player netted for Manchester United against Wimbledon from inside his own half on the opening day of the 1996-97 season?

4. WHO was the Wimbledon keeper in that game?

5. IN season 1982-83, which Ajax player, when taking a penalty, played a 1-2 with Jesper Olsen before scoring instead of taking a direct kick?

6. WHO scored for Hibs against Morton with a direct kick-out in 1988?

7. WHO scored over Tim Flowers' shoulder for Liverpool against Blackburn in 1995 after the ball had spun up from a divot, causing Flowers to burst out laughing?

8. WHO scored for Scotland against England in 1975 by stroking the ball through Ray Clemence's legs?

9. WHICH goalkeeper scored an own goal for Leeds United against Rangers in the 1992 European Cup?

10. WHO scored for Coventry against Everton in 1970 after team-mate Willie Carr flicked the ball up with both feet, a move later outlawed?

ANSWERS: Turn to page 101

Getting Shirty

WHO are the shirt sponsors of the following football clubs?

1. Fulham.

2. Motherwell.

3. Airdrie.

4. Kilmarnock.

5. Hibernian.

6. St Johnstone.

7. Chelsea.

8. Dundee.

9. Aberdeen.

10. Hearts.

ANSWERS: Turn to page 101

ANSWERS

Equestrian

ANSWERS

1. Joe Fargis;
2. Alwin Shockemohle;
3. Ian Stark;
4. Michael and John Whittaker;
5. Mary Chapot;
6. Nick Skelton;
7. Liz Edgar;
8. Eddie Macken;
9. Malcolm Pyrah;
10. Hartwig Steenken.

All American Show

ANSWERS

1. American Football;
2. Roger Kingdom;
3. Roy Jones;
4. Showjumping;
5. The outstanding college player of the year;
6. New York Mets;
7. USSR;
8. Philadelphia Phillies;
9. Pine tar, to improve grip;
10. Joe Di Maggio.

Just for Keeps

ANSWERS

1. Javier Sanchez Broto;
2. Marco Ruitenbeek;
3. Tony Parks;
4. Paul Mathers;
5. Bristol Rovers;
6. Danish;
7. Toulouse, Marseille and Monaco;
8. Vitesse;
9. Wolves;
10. Jim Brown.

Strange Goals in Football

1. Jim Fryatt;
2. Nayim;
3. David Beckham;
4. Neil Sullivan;
5. Johan Cruyff;
6. Andy Goram;
7. Stan Collymore;
8. Kenny Dalglish;
9. John Lukic;
10. Ernie Hunt.

Getting Shirty

1. Pizza Hut;
2. Motorola;
3. ScotShield;
4. Seriously Strong;
5. Carlsberg;
6. Xara;
7. Autoglass;
8. Ceramic Tile Warehouse;
9. A-Fab;
10. Strongbow.

Mixed Bag (2)

1. WHO won his fourth successive men's Olympics discus title in 1968?
2. WHO, in 1956, became the first winner of the European Footballer of the Year Award?
3. WHICH Czech won the men's tennis singles title and gold medal at the 1988 Olympics?
4. WHAT colour does Tiger Woods traditionally wear on the last day of a golf tournament?
5. DURING his successful days, what colour did Seve Ballesteros traditionally wear on the last day of a golf event?
6. WHICH Pakistani leg-spinner took a wicket with his first ball in Test cricket in 1959-60?
7. HOW did American golfer Lee Elder make golfing history in the Ryder Cup in 1979?
8. WHERE are the most expensive seats in a bull-fighting stadium?
9. KORFBALL is a game mixed between netball and basketball. Where did it originate?
10. WHO was the BBC's first football correspondent on television?

ANSWERS: Turn to page 107

Football: World Cup (2)

1. WHICH country used only 12 players in winning the 1962 World Cup?

2. WHO is the only player to have scored in successive World Cup Finals?

3. WHICH country scored a record 25 goals in six matches to win the 1954 World Cup?

4. WHO was sent off after just 55 seconds for Uruguay against Scotland in the 1986 World Cup finals?

5. WHO, with 14 goals, is the highest scorer in World Cup history?

6. WHY was the 1974 World Cup Final between West Germany and Holland delayed?

7. WHICH Englishman refereed that final?

8. ONLY two players have featured in five World Cup finals. Name both.

9. WHO, in the 1974 World Cup, became the first player to score from the spot in the final?

10. WHICH Scot set a Home Countries record when he scored in five World Cup qualifying matches during the 1990 campaign?

ANSWERS: Turn to page 108

Cups, Trophies, Prizes

1. WHAT would you be playing if you were participating in the Iroquois Cup?

2. IN what sport is the Eisenhower Trophy a major prize?

3. IN ice hockey, to whom is the Conn-Smythe Trophy awarded?

4. WHAT trophy, originally called the Hundred Guineas Cup, was offered in 1851 to the winner of a race round the Isle of Wight?

5. IN which sport do women compete for the Uber Cup?

-6-
IN which sport do countries compete for the Bruno Zauli Trophy?

7. WHO compete for the Swaythling Cup?

8. FOR what sport is the W.K. Lennard Trophy an important prize?

9. WHAT was rugby union's Calcutta Cup made from?

10. IN which sport was a competition, which originated in 1953 as the Canada Cup, made into the World Cup.

ANSWERS: Turn to page 108

Foreign Footballers in Scotland

1. WHAT nationality is St Johnstone's Nick Dasovic?

2. FROM which side did Rangers sign Michael Mols?

3. NAME the first current Livingston player to be signed from Italian club Brescia?

4. From which side did Kilmarnock sign Spaniard Jesus Garcia Sanjuan?

5. WHAT nationality is Hibs' Ulrik Laursen?

-6-
From which side did Hearts sign Frenchman Stephane Adam?

7. WHICH club did Hearts' Juanjo play for before moving to Tynecastle?

8. WHAT nationality is Dundee's Georgi Nemsadze?

9. FROM which team did Celtic sign Lubomir Moravcik?

10. WHICH club did Bobo Balde play for before he joined Celtic?

ANSWERS: Turn to page 109

Sport in the 1980s

1. FROM which nation were Red Boys Differdange national football cup winners in 1982?

2. WHICH athlete, having never run the distance, won the 1980 New York Marathon?

3. NAME two of the four FA Cup semi-finalists in 1984?

4. WHO, in 1983, became the first Frenchman to win the French Open tennis title since 1946?

5. WHO, in 1985, became only the second cricketer to score six sixes in an over in a first class game?

6. WHICH golfer – son of a famous entertainer – won the US Amateur Golf Championship in 1982?

7. WHO retained his WBC heavyweight boxing title by stopping Gerry Cooney in 1982?

8. WHICH Dutch cyclist won the Tour de France in 1980?

9. WHICH American golfer won the US Masters for the first time in 1984?

10. WHICH English cricketer, now an international umpire, took six wickets AGAINST England on the New Zealand tour of 1983-84?

ANSWERS: Turn to page 109

ANSWERS

Mixed Bag (2)

ANSWERS

1. Al Oerter;
2. Stanley Matthews;
3. Miroslav Mecir;
4. Red;
5. Blue;
6. Intikhab Alam;
7. He became the first black player to play for the US in the competition;
8. In the shade;
9. Holland;
10. Brian Moore.

Football: World Cup (2)

ANSWERS

1.   Brazil;
2.   Vava, 1958 (twice) and 1962;
3.   West Germany;
4.   Jose Batista;
5.   Gerd Muller;
6.   There were no corner flags;
7.   Jack Taylor (Wolverhampton);
8.   Antonio Carbajal, Mexico, and
       Lothar Matthaus, Germany;
9.   Johan Neeskens;
10.   Mo Johnston.

Cups, Trophies, Prizes

ANSWERS

1.   Lacrosse;
2.   Golf - World Amateur
       Championship;
3.   MVP in the Stanley Cup;
4.   The Americas Cup;
5.   Badminton;
6.   Athletics;
7.   Men's table tennis;
8.   World bowls;
9.   Indian Rupees;
10.   Golf.

Foreign Footballers in Scotland

ANSWERS

1. Canadian;
2. FC Utrecht;
3. Massimiliano Caputo;
4. Airdrie;
5. Danish;
6. Metz;
7. Barcelona;
8. Georgian;
9. MSV Duisburg;
10. Toulouse.

Sport in the 1980s

ANSWERS

1. Luxembourg;
2. Alberto Salazar;
3. Everton, Watford, Southampton and Plymouth;
4. Yannick Noah;
5. Ravi Shastri (India);
6. Nat Crosby (son of Bing);
7. Larry Holmes;
8. Joop Zoetemelk;
9. Ben Crenshaw;
10. Neil Mallande – for Otago.

Foreign Fields

WHICH famous clubs are these venues associated with?

1. The Letna Stadium

2. The Stadio delle Alpi

3. The Amsterdam Arena

4. Stadio Bombonera, Argentina

5. The Westfalenstadion

6. Vicente Calderon

7. Parc Astrid

8. Vila Belmiro, Brazil

9. Philips Stadium

10. The De Kuyp Stadium

ANSWERS: Turn to page 115

Great Scots

1. WHICH Scot won the 1999 world indoor men's singles bowls title?

2. WHICH Scottish racehorse trainer was known as The Benign Bishop?

3. WHICH Scottish sprinter won the men's 100 metres gold medal at the 1982 Commonwealth Games?

4. IN that same race, which fellow Scot took the bronze medal?

5. WHICH Scotsmen won the badminton doubles gold medals at the 1986 Commonwealth Games in Edinburgh?

6. IN which year did Tom Imrie win boxing gold for Scotland at the Commonwealth Games?

7. WHO captained the Scottish cricket team in the 1999 World Cup finals?

8. IN those finals, how many games did Scotland win?

9. IN which sport was Barry Robertson a Scottish legend?

10. WILLIE Wood, David Gourlay, Jim Boyle, Brian Rattray and Doug Lambert were overall world champions in 1984 in which sport?

ANSWERS: Turn to page 116

Ice 'n' Easy

1. IN ice hockey, how many players from each side are allowed on the ice at any one time?
2. IN which sport would you find a brakeman?
3. WHICH countries contest the Stanley Cup?
4. FOR which country did Hanni Wenzel ski?

-5-
IN what sport do the contestants score marks for a loop and a rocker?

6. PHIL Mahre was 1981 World Champion and his brother Steve was fourth, but in which sport?
7. WHICH Italian skiier was nickamed La Bomba?
8. WHICH two events make up the Nordic combined?
9. WHICH Norwegian won the 1999 men's World Combined skiing title?
10. WHICH character from Shakespeare's play 'A Midsummer Night's Dream' shares his name with a piece of equipment used in a sport on ice?

ANSWERS: Turn to page 116

The Summer Game

1. WHO was the England cricket captain who turned down a place at Oxford University?

2. WHICH Scot succeeded Ray Illingworth as captain of the English cricket team in 1973?

3. TO whose memory is the pavilion at Parker's Piece, Cambridge, dedicated?

4. WHICH former England captain was involved in the 1985 'Find a Fast Bowler' competition?

5. WHAT was the name of Ian Botham and Alan Lamb's comedy show which toured Britain?

6. FORMER Prime Minister John Major is a member of which county?

7. WHICH football team does ex-England captain Alec Stewart follow?

8. WHICH brilliant Pakistani batsman in 1983 became the 20th to score 100 first-class centuries?

9. WHO was the first Englishman to average 100 runs in a season?

10. WHICH Lancastrian cricketer took 252 wickets in only 70 Tests?

ANSWERS: Turn to page 117

Mixed Bag (3)

1. WITH which sport would you associate former Hungarian acrobat Joe Turi?

2. WHICH track staged the first British motor racing Grand Prix in 1926?

3. WHO was the only Indian cricketer to appear in the MCC side for the Bi-Centenary match at Lord's in 1987?

4. HIS father was a singer, his mother an actress and his sister shot JR and he was the 1981 US Amateur Golf Champion. Name the family?

5. IN which sport did Janet Evans break two world records in 1987?

6. RUGBY Union – Who captained France in 1977 and coached them to Grand Slams in 1981 and 1987?

7. IN which sport are blue and black always partners against red and yellow?

8. IN which sport is the only obstacle 3'6" high?

9. WHO captained the Irish rugby union team to the Triple Crown in 1981?

10. WHICH English league football club signed Danish internationalist and newly appointed Luxembourg manager, Allan Simonsen, in 1982?

ANSWERS: Turn to page 117

ANSWERS

Foreign Fields

ANSWERS

1.   Sparta Prague;
2.   Juventus;
3.   Ajax;
4.   Boca Juniors;
5.   Borussia Dortmund;
6.   Atletico Madrid;
7.   Anderlecht;
8.   Santos;
9.   PSV Eindhoven;
10.   Feyenoord.

Great Scots

1. Alex Marshall;
2. Ken Oliver;
3. Allan Wells;
4. Cameron Sharp;
5. Dan Travers and Billy Gilliland;
6. 1970;
7. George Salmond;
8. None;
9. Volleyball;
10. Bowls.

Ice 'n' Easy

1. Six;
2. Bobsleigh;
3. American and Canadian ice hockey champions;
4. Liechtenstein;
5. Ice skating;
6. Alpine Skiiing;
7. Alberto Tomba;
8. Cross-country skiing and ski jumping;
9. Kjell Aamodt;
10. Puck.

The Summer Game

ANSWERS

1. David Gower;
2. Mike Denness;
3. Sir Jack Hobbs;
4. Ted Dexter;
5. Beefy and Lamb in a Stew;
6. Surrey;
7. Chelsea;
8. Zaheer Abbas;
9. Geoff Boycott;
10. Brian Statham.

Mixed Bag (3)

ANSWERS

1. Showjumping;
2. Brooklands, Surrey;
3. Ravi Shastri;
4. The Crosbys — Nathanial was the golfer and Bing the dad;
5. Swimming;
6. Jacques Foroux;
7. Croquet;
8. Tennis, the height of the net;
9. Ciaran Fitzgerald;
10. Charlton Athletic.

Boxing

1. WHICH Brit challenged Muhammad Ali for the world heavyweight title in Munich in 1976?

2. WHICH boxer, who won an Olympic middle-weight gold medal in 1976, went on to win professional world titles at both light heavyweight and heavyweight?

3. WHO won the super heavyweight gold medal for Britain at the 2000 Olympic Games?

4. WHO won gold in the light heavyweight division at the 1976 Olympics in Montreal?

5. WHICH Cuban won gold in the heavyweight division at three successive Olympics, from 1972 to 1980?

6. WHO won the light-weight gold medal for the USA at the 1976 Olympic Games and later lost to Scotland's Jim Watt in a professional World title fight?

7. WHICH Scot won the 1956 Olympic light-weight boxing gold medal?

8. WHICH boxer won gold at middleweight in 1948 and gold at light middleweight in both 1952 and 1956?

9. WHO won the super heavyweight gold medal for Canada at the 1988 Olympics in Seoul?

10. WHICH American took the Olympic super heavyweight gold medal in Los Angeles in 1984?

ANSWERS: Turn to page 123

Darts

1. WHAT is the only two-figure number that cannot be finished in two darts?

2. WHO, in 1978, was the first World Professional Darts champions?

3. WHO was the first man to win both the World Masters and the British Open in the same year?

4. WHAT is the highest out-shot with three darts?

5. WHO did Eric Bristow beat to win his first Embassy World Professional Darts title?

6. WHO, in 1979, became the first overseas player to win a World Cup individual title?

-7-
NAME the Scotsman who won the World Darts title in 1982?

8. IN that same year the Scot won the British Open as well, but lost in the final of the World Masters. Who beat him?

9. WHO was the first man to lose in two World Professional darts finals in successive years?

10. WHAT is the minimum number of darts required to score 1001?

ANSWERS: Turn to page 124

Mix 'n' Match

1. IN which two sports might you use a spoon?

2. WHO won the men's 5,000 metres at the 1984 Olympics?

3. WHO led India to victory at the 1983 cricket World Cup?

4. WOODBINE and Randwick are famous horse-racing courses. In which countries would you find them?

5. NAME either of the two sides who contested the 1985 Superbowl?

6. WHICH famous character partnered Rosie Casals to victory in the mixed doubles at Wimbledon in both 1970 and 1972?

7. WHICH player scored for both sides in the 1981 English FA Cup final at Wembley?

8. WHO, between 1969 and 1981, became Wales' most capped rugby union international?

9. WHICH club won the 1999 SRU Tennents Cup in rugby union?

10. WHO won the 1999 World Matchplay Darts championship?

ANSWERS: Turn to page 124

Animal Magic

1. IN British greyhound racing, what colour of jacket is always worn by the dog in trap two?

2. SCOT Ian Stark won the 1999 Badminton three-day event trials, but on which horse?

3. WHICH horse won the 1999 Budweiser Irish Derby?

---

4. WHICH horse finished third in the 2000 Grand National?

---

5. WHICH horse was ridden by Tony McCoy in the 2000 Grand National?

6. WHICH horse won the 1999 Juddmonte International Stakes at York?

7. WAS Patricia's Hope a famous racehorse or greyhound?

8. WHAT was the name of the dog that found the World Cup when it went missing after England had won it in 1966?

9. WHICH horse won the 2000 Grand National?

10. WHO rode the winner of the 2000 Grand National?

ANSWERS: Turn to page 125

Famous Stadiums

1. WHICH stadium, opened in 1947, hosted the 1964 European championship final when Spain beat the Soviet Union 2-1?

2. NAME the stadium that hosted both the 1970 and 1986 World Cup finals.

3. ONE stadium hosted both the 1984 Olympic football final and the 1994 World Cup final – name it.

4. WHICH stadium is shared by Botafago, Vasco da Gama, Flamengo and Fluminese?

5. WHICH stadium hosted the 1948 Olympic football final when Sweden beat Yugoslavia 3-1?

6. WHICH stadium in Portugal held both the 1991 World Youth Cup final and the 1992 European Cup Winners' Cup final?

7. IT held the European Cup Final in 1960 and again in 1976, and in 2002 is due to host the Champions League Cup Final. Where is it?

8. WHAT was the venue for the 1936 Olympic Final and, in 1974, group matches in the World Cup finals?

9. IN 1992 the Olympic football final was held there, while in 1989 A.C. Milan won the European Cup in this stadium. Where?

10. IN which stadium did Feyenoord beat Celtic 2-1 in the European Cup Final in 1970?

ANSWERS: Turn to page 125

ANSWERS

Boxing

ANSWERS

1. Richard Dunn;
2. Michael Spinks;
3. Audley Harrison;
4. Leon Spinks;
5. Teophilio Stevenson;
6. Howard Davis;
7. Dick McTaggart;
8. Laszlo Papp of Hungary;
9. Lennox Lewis;
10. Tyrell Biggs.

Darts

1. 99;
2. Leighton Rees;
3. Alan Evans, 1975;
4. 170;
5. Bobby George;
6. Nicky Virachkul;
7. Jocky Wilson;
8. Dave Whitcombe;
9. John Lowe;
10. 17.

Mix 'n' Match

ANSWERS

1. Golf and fishing;
2. Said Aouita;
3. Kapil Dev;
4. Canada (Woodbine),
    Australia (Randwick);
5. Miami Dolphins, San Francisco 49rs;
6. Ilie Nastase;
7. Tommy Hutchison (Manchester City);
8. J.P.R. Williams;
9. Gala;
10. Rod Harrington.

Animal Magic

1. Blue;
2. Jaybee;
3. Montjeu;
4. Niki Dee;
5. Dark Stranger;
6. Royal Anthem;
7. A greyhound;
8. Pickles;
9. Papillon;
10. Ruby Walsh.

Famous Stadiums

1. Santiago Bernabeu;
2. Azteca or Estadio Guillermo Canedo;
3. Rose Bowl, Pasadena;
4. Maracana;
5. Wembley;
6. Estadio Da Luz, Lisbon;
7. Hampden Park, Glasgow;
8. Olympic Stadium, Berlin;
9. Nou Camp, Barcelona;
10. San Siro, Milan, aka the Giuseppe Meazza.

Mystery Footballers

1.   BORN in Chester-le-Street, Co Durham; In 1984 became first England captain to score a hat-trick for 75 years; Appointed player-manager of Middlesbrough in 1994.

2.   BORN in 1966 in Rio de Janeiro; Scored five goals for Brazil in the 1994 World Cup finals.

3.   BORN in South Shields in 1921; Scored Blackpool's second goal in the 1948 FA Cup Final; In 1953 became the first player to score a hat-trick in a Wembley Final.

4.   BORN in Airdrie in 1893. Won his first championship title with Rangers in 1921; Played 495 games for Rangers and was a member of the 1929 Wembley Wizards.

5.   BORN in Glasgow in September 1962; Left minor football and joined St Johnstone in 1978; Voted Scotland's Player of the Year and won Europe's Golden Boot in 1992.

6.   BORN in Blantyre in March, 1940; Made the first of more than 500 senior appearances for his club in 1959; Lifted the European Cup for Celtic in 1967.

7.   Born in County Down, Northern Ireland, in 1945; An FA Cup winner with Spurs in 1967 and scored in Charity Shield in same year; Won his 119th cap for Northern Ireland on his 41st birthday in 1986.

ANSWERS: Turn to page 131

Around the World

1. WHICH country won the 1999 World Team Fly Fishing championships?

2. THE 1999 Women's World Curling champions came from which country?

3. WHO was the Dutchman who won the BDO World Darts championship in 1999?

4. NAME the club that won the 1999 Australian Rules Grand Final?

5. WHICH teams met in the 1999 All Ireland Gaelic football final?

6. WHO were French football league champions in 2000-01?

7. WHICH club lifted the Belgian league title in season 2000-01?

8. WHICH club took the Portuguese league in 2000-01 – one point ahead of Porto?

9. WHICH city hosted the 2000 Olympic Games?

10. FROM which country does tennis player Michael Chang come?

ANSWERS: Turn to page 132

The Hot Seat

AT the start of the 2001-02 season, who was in the manager's hot seat at the following English clubs?

1.   Watford.

2.   Crystal Palace.

3.   Wycombe Wanderers.

4.   Millwall

5.   Huddersfield Town.

6.   Fulham

7.   Burnley

8.   Middlesbrough

9.   Nottingham Forest

10.   Plymouth Argyle

ANSWERS: Turn to page 132

Driving Force

1. WHO, in 1980, became the youngest winner of the US Masters golf tournament?

2. WHICH British golfer was within one shot of tying for the 1982 Open at Royal Troon?

3. TURNBERRY, Ailsa and the Well are all holes on which British Open championship course?

4. WHICH player won £50,000 for a hole in one at the 1979 World matchplay championship at Wentworth?

5. WHO won the 1961 US Amateur golf title and the US Open the following year at the age of 22?

6. WHO won the Heritage Classic in 1985 to become the first European golfer to lift back-to-back events on the US tour?

7. WHICH unattached British golf professional came fourth in the 1980 British Open behind three Americans?

8. IN 1980, Jack Nicklaus won his fourth US Open. Who was the previous golfer to achieve that feat?

9. WHICH British golfer in the 1974 US Masters equalled the record round in the championship?

10. IN the 1983 World Matchplay championship, which golfer was helped by a cheating spectator who threw his ball back on to the green after it had run into the crowd?

ANSWERS: Turn to page 133

World Football

1. FROM which French club did George Weah move to Paris Saint-Germain?

2. IN which African country were Goldfields league champions from 1994 to 1996?

3. HOW old was Argentinian forward Angel Labruna when he played in the 1958 World Cup finals?

-4-
WHO was the first US professional to play in Italy's Serie A?

5. WHICH country won the 1992 Asian Cup?

6. IN which African country were Gor Mahia league champions from 1983 to 1985?

7. FOR which Dutch club did Nwankwo Kanu play?

8. IN which year was Argentinian striker Mario Kempes born?

9. IN which year did Mexican striker Hugo Sanchez make his World Cup Finals debut?

10. WHAT was Brazilian goalkeeper Claudio Taffarel's first club in Italy?

ANSWERS: Turn to page 133

ANSWERS

Mystery Footballers

ANSWERS

1. Bryan Robson;
2. Romario;
3. Stan Mortensen;
4. Alan Morton;
5. Ally McCoist;
6. Billy McNeill;
7. Pat Jennings.

Around the World

1.   Australia;
2.   Sweden;
3.   Raymond van Barneveld;
4.   Adelaide Crows;
5.   Kerry and Mayo;
6.   Nantes;
7.   Anderlecht;
8.   Boavista;
9.   Sydney;
10.   America.

The Hot Seat

1.   Gianluca Vialli;
2.   Steve Bruce;
3.   Lawrie Sanchez;
4.   Mark McGhee;
5.   Lou Macari;
6.   Jean Tigana;
7.   Stan Ternent;
8.   Steve McClaren;
9.   Paul Hart;
10.   Paul Sturrock.

Driving Force

ANSWERS

1. Seve Ballesteros;
2. Peter Oosterhuis;
3. Troon;
4. Isao Aoki;
5. Jack Nicklaus;
6. Bernhard Langer;
7. Carl Mason;
8. Ben Hogan;
9. Maurice Bembridge;
10. Nick Faldo.

World Football

ANSWERS

1. Monaco;
2. Ghana;
3. 40;
4. Alexi Lalas;
5. Japan;
6. Kenya;
7. Ajax;
8. 1952;
9. 1978;
10. Parma.

Just hit it and hope

NOW is your chance to make the back page headlines. The ball drops to you 40 yards out and you spot the goalie off his line. Well, if you don't buy a ticket you won't win the raffle, so here's a final selection of long shots ....

Real Stinkers

1. Only one non-league club has won the English FA Cup this centur – back in 1901? Name the team.

2. WHICH country did Australia beat 31-0 in a World Cup qualifier in 2001?

3. IN which year did Kenny Dalglish win the first of his 102 Scottish caps?

4. WHAT did Scottish international footballers Tommy Craig, Jimmy Smith and Mark McGhee all have in common?

5. WHEN was the last time tug-of-war was an Olympic sport?

6. WHO is the president of Preston North End?

7. FOR what did Boris Onischenko become infamous at the 1976 Olympics in Montreal?

8. WHICH sport originated in Italy, is otherwise known as Jai Alai, and is said to be the fastest ball game in the world?

9. WHICH two events were demonstration sports at the 1984 Los Angeles Olympics?

10. IN 1929, hollow wood was allowed. In 1956, light plastic foam was permitted. What sport?

ANSWERS: Turn to page 141

Cricket, Lovely Cricket

1. WHICH brilliant, slow left-arm Indian spinner was out for a duck 20 times as a batsman in 67 Test innings?

2. WHO, in Wisden's Five Cricketers of the Century, came out on top with 100 per cent of the votes?

3. WHO scored 131 on his Test debut for India against England at Lord's in 1996?

4. IN that same match, which famous umpire made his last Test appearance?

5. WHO was his partner on that occasion?

6. WHICH famous cricketer's first names were Isaac Vivian Alexander?

7. OF his 18 Test centuries for England, how many did David Gower score against Australia?

8. IN which year was Brian Lara born?

9. WHICH Australian scored 1575 runs for Yorkshire in the 1997 Britannic Assurance County Championship?

10. IN which Australian city did Scot Mike Denness score his only Test century for England against Australia?

ANSWERS: Turn to page 142

Mixed Bag (4)

1. IN January 2000, who were rated the third best team in Europe in the FIFA football world rankings?

2. WHICH legendary American jockey won the 1987 Breeders Cup Classic on Ferdinand?

3. WHO was leading the 1949 British Open golf championship when his ball landed on a broken beer bottle?

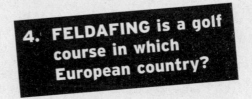

4. FELDAFING is a golf course in which European country?

5. IN which Caribbean city in January 1973 did Joe Frazier fight George Foreman?

6. IN which summer Olympic Games did Australian Betty Cuthbert win four gold medals?

7. WHICH city will host the 2002 Commonwealth Games?

8. DEREK Bell and which former Belgian F1 driver won the 1976 Le Mans 24 hour race?

9. WHO rode Petite Etoile to victory in the 1960 Coronation Cup?

10. WHAT was unusual about the 1884 Epsom Derby?

ANSWERS: Turn to page 142

Horse Racing

1. WHICH horse won the 1999 July Cup at Newmarket?

2. WHICH horse won the 1999 King George VI and Queen Elizabeth Diamond Stakes?

3. WHICH horse won the 1999 St Leger?

4. WHICH two jockeys each rode four winners at Royal Ascot in 1999?

5. WHO rode Bobbyjo in the 2000 Aintree Grand National?

6. WHO was the top flat race jockey in Britain in 1999?

7. WHO was the champion Flat trainer in Britain in 1999?

8. WHICH horse, in 1985, gave Steve Cauthen his first Epsom Derby win?

9. TRUE or False. Champion Hurdle winner Sea Pigeon once ran on the Flat at Hamilton Park?

10. HENRY Cecil trained the Goodwood Cup winner three years in succession, including twice with the same horse. Which horse?

ANSWERS: Turn to page 143

British Football

1. NAME the chairman of Kilmarnock FC.

2. WHO succeeded Alan MacDonald as chief executive of Celtic?

3. HE was manager of Watford from 1977 to 1987 and again from 1997 to 2001. Name him.

4. WHO was manager of Port Vale from 1984 until 1999?

5. WHEN was the last season Manchester United finished outwith the top two in the English Premiership or old First Division?

6. WHO scored a hat-trick for Manchester United in a 6-1 win over Arsenal to clinch the 1951-52 league title?

7. WHO did David O'Leary succeed as manager of Leeds United in 1998?

8. NAME the boss of Arsenal before Arsene Wenger stepped into the hot seat.

9. WHO made 76 appearances in Europe for Dundee United, a record for a Scottish player?

10. WITH 13 caps for the Republic of Ireland, who is Motherwell's most capped player?

ANSWERS: Turn to page 143

ANSWERS

Real Stinkers

ANSWERS

1.   Tottenham Hotspur;
2.   American Samoa;
3.   1971;
4.   They all played for both Aberdeen
      and Newcastle United;
5.   1920;
6.   Sir Tom Finney;
7.   He cheated at fencing;
8.   Pelota;
9.   Baseball and Tennis;
10.   Surfing.

Cricket, Lovely Cricket

ANSWERS

1. Bishen Bedi;
2. Sir Don Bradman;
3. Saurav Ganguly;
4. Dickie Bird;
5. Darrell Hair (Australia);
6. Viv Richards;
7. Nine;
8. 1969;
9. Darren Leymann;
10. Melbourne.

Mixed Bag (4)

ANSWERS

1. Spain;
2. Bill Shoemaker;
3. Harry Bradshaw;
4. Germany;
5. Kingston, Jamaica;
6. Melbourne 1956;
7. Manchester;
8. Jacky Ickx;
9. Lester Piggott;
10. It was a dead heat between St Gatien and Harvester.

Horse Racing

1. Stravinsky;
2. Daylami;
3. Mutafaweq;
4. Frankie Dettori and Mick Kinane;
5. Paul Carberry;
6. Kieren Fallon;
7. Saeed bin Suroor;
8. Slip Anchor;
9. True;
10. Le Moss, 1979 and 1980.

British Football

1. Sir John Orr;
2. Ian McLeod;
3. Graham Taylor;
4. John Rudge;
5. 1990-91;
6. Jack Rowley;
7. George Graham;
8. Bruce Rioch;
9. David Narey;
10. Tommy Coyne.

Rules & Regulations (1)

1. HOW many lanes are there in an Olympic swimming pool?
2. HOW many players make up a roller hockey team?
3. WHAT is the maximum number of gates in a men's slalom skiing competition?
4. WHAT is the height, in inches, of a table tennis net?

-5-
WHAT is the total playing time in a game of polo?

6. A MEN'S lacrosse game comprises four quarters of what duration?
7. IN cricket, what is the last thing an umpire does before the bowler bowls the first ball of a match?
8. WHAT does a blue flag mean in a motorcycle race?
9. HOW long does a game of shinty last?
10. WHAT is the maximum weight, in ounces, of a hockey stick?

ANSWERS: Turn to page 149

Rugby Union

1. WHO was the Welsh rugby union star who was also junior Wimbledon tennis champion in 1966?

2. ENGLISH full-back Dusty Hare played for which club?

3. WHICH schoolboy player at Rugby school is usually credited with first picking up the ball and playing rugby?

4. WHICH was the only divisional side to beat the All Blacks on their tour of Britain in 1978?

5. IN which country are the world's highest rugby posts?

6. IN which month each year is the University varsity match played?

7. BEFORE Dusty Hare, which Harlequins full-back held England's points-scoring record?

8. WHICH north of England side play in green and white hooped shirts?

9. UP to the end of 1985, who was France's most capped internationalist?

10. WHO scored a hat-trick of tries for England against Scotland at Murrayfield in 1980?

ANSWERS: Turn to page 150

Sport in the 1970s

1. WHO, in 1977, became the first player to reach the Wimbledon semi-finals as a pre-tournament qualifier?

2. WHICH player, after winning the World Chess Championship, was awarded the City of New York Medal in 1972?

3. WHO managed the West German football side to victory in the 1974 World Cup?

4. NAME the winner of the 1972 British Open Golf Championship.

5. WHO was voted European Footballer of the Year in 1973?

6. WHICH Celtic player went rowing during Scotland's preparations for the 1974 World Cup finals?

7. WHAT popular phrase was taken up by Spurs supporters in 1973 to create a hit song?

8. IN 1971, captain Alan Shepherd hit a golf ball in an unusual place. Where?

9. WHICH sports film won the Oscar for best picture in 1976?

10. WHO won the Badminton three-day event two years running in 1971 and 1972?

ANSWERS: Turn to page 150

Unusual Records & Events

1. WHICH BBC commentator won the Manchester mile race in 1949?

2. HOW were the entire Japanese wrestling team at the 1960 Rome Olympics punished for their poor performances?

3. WHY did a match between Leicester City and Stockport County in 1923 enter the record books?

4. FRED Lorz was the first man to cross the line in the 1904 Olympic marathon but was then disqualified. Why?

5. WHAT was the score in the Borg/McEnroe tie-break in the 1980 men's Wimbledon final?

6. WHICH footballer, later England manager, released a record called Head Over Heels in Love?

7. WHY were AC Milan and Lazio relegated to the Second Division in 1980?

8. WHICH ex-Surrey and England off-spinner once took five wickets with six balls?

9. WHERE was the world's first floodlit football match held?

10. WHICH former British Olympic gold medallist was race director of the London Marathon when it began in 1981?

ANSWERS: Turn to page 151

Scottish Football

1. WHAT nationality is Aberdeen's Hicham Zerouali?

2. FROM which Belgian club did Hibs sign Alen Orman?

3. HIBS' Frederic Arpinon left the French team who knocked Newcastle out of the 2001 Inter-Toto Cup. Name the team.

4. FROM which Scottish club did Kilmarnock sign Ally Mitchell?

5. WHO is chairman of Motherwell?

6. WHO, with nine goals, was St Johnstone's top league goalscorer in season 2000-01?

7. WHO was Livingston's leading league goalscorer in 2000-01, helping them win promotion and the First Division championship?

8. TWO players shared the honour of Hearts' leading league scorers in season 2000/01. Colin Cameron was one, who was the other?

9. GARETH Hutchison was a top scorer in season 2000-01, but for which club?

10. WHO was an ever present in goal for East Stirlingshire in season 2000-01?

ANSWERS: Turn to page 151

ANSWERS

Rules & Regulations (1)

ANSWERS

1.   Eight;
2.   Five;
3.   75;
4.   Six inches;
5.   56 minutes;
6.   25 minutes;
7.   Call play;
8.   Rider behind;
9.   90 minutes;
10.   28 ounces.

Rugby Union

1.   J.P.R. Williams:
2.   Leicester Tigers;
3.   William Webb Ellis;
4.   Munster;
5.   South Africa;
6.   December;
7.   Bob Hiller;
8.   Gosforth;
9.   Roland Bertranne;
10. John Carleton, of Orrell.

Sport in the 1970s

ANSWERS

1.   John McEnroe;
2.   Bobby Fischer;
3.   Helmut Schoen;
4.   Lee Trevino;
5.   Franz Beckenbauer;
6.   Jimmy Johnstone;
7.   Nice One Cyril;
8.   On the moon;
9.   Rocky;
10. Captain Mark Phillips.

Unusual Records & Events

ANSWERS

1.   David Coleman;
2.   Their heads were shaved;
3.   It attracted a crowd of 13;
4.   He caught a lift in a car;
5.   18-16 to McEnroe;
6.   Kevin Keegan;
7.   For allegedly fixing results;
8.   Pat Pocock;
9.   Bramall Lane, Sheffield, in 1878;
10.   Chris Brasher.

Scottish Football

ANSWERS

1.   Moroccan;
2.   Royal Antwerp;
3.   Troyes;
4.   East Fife;
5.   John Boyle;
6.   Keigan Parker;
7.   David Bingham;
8.   Andy Kirk;
9.   Falkirk;
10.   Jim Butter.

After Eights

1. WHICH horse was winner of the 1923 Grand National at the age of 13?

2. NAME the boxer who was WBC light heavy-weight champion in 1994 and 1995?

3. WHICH Czech tennis player was second top of the women's world rankings in 1996?

4. WHAT nationality is motor racing driver Roberto Moreno?

5. OUT of 23 games in the World Cup finals from 1930 to 1998, how many have Scotland actually won?

6. THE modern rules for bowls were drawn up by a solicitor from which British city?

7. WHAT was the nickname of boxer Max Baer?

8. WHICH Irishman, who was the sixth president of the International Olympic Committee, died in April 1999?

9. WHO retired as president of the IOC after the 2000 Olympic Games?

10. NAME the boxer who won the British heavy-weight title in 1957 – 13 years after his father had held the same title?

ANSWERS: Turn to page 157

Athletics

1. WHICH man won silver medals in both the 5,000 and 10,000 metres at the 1983 World Championships?

2. THE first Olympic women's marathon took place in 1984. Who won the event?

3. WHICH Scottish girl appeared in an Olympic relay final in Moscow at the age of 16?

4. THE girl who finished third behind Mary Peters in the 1972 pentathlon also took the bronze four years later. Who was she?

5. WHO, in 1980, became the first woman to run the 1,500 metres faster than Paavo Nurmi?

6. WHO won the men's 5,000 metres gold medal in the 1978 European Championships and also took silver in the 10,000 metres?

7. WHICH middle-distance athlete was the first to go under three minutes 50 seconds for the mile?

8. WHOSE long-standing 100 metres world record was broken by Calvin Smith in July 1983?

9. WHICH East German was the first girl to win two Olympic golds in the javelin?

10. WHICH American won the 1976 decathlon gold at the Olympics and later starred in the movie Can't Stop the Music with The Village People?

ANSWERS: Turn to page 158

Lucky Dip

1. IN which event did seven shoes and a sock bring Britain a gold medal at the 1986 European Athletics Championships?

2. WHAT must not be less than 186 miles or more than 198.8 miles and must not go on for more than two hours?

3. HIS birth name was Joe Sholto Douglas but under which name did he write his way into the record books?

4. WHAT sport would you be watching if a fireman came on as a relief?

5. WHAT is the lowest number you CANNOT score with a single dart?

6. WHICH sport has a beach start and a dock start?

7. BETWEEN which two sides is the Bowring Bowl contested annually?

8. IN which sport did Cameron and Waldo of Canada become world champions in Madrid in 1986 and Commonwealth Games champions the same year?

9. WHICH major British sporting event has been won by an Anglo, a Russian Hero and a Wild Man of Borneo?

10. IF the Maple Leafs were playing the Saracens, which sport in Britain would you be watching?

ANSWERS: Turn to page 158

Rules & Regulations (2)

1. IN cricket, can the groundsman water the pitch during an interval after the match has started?

2. WHAT is the minimum age of a horse in Flat racing?

3. WHAT is the name given to a stick used in hurling?

4. HOW high, in metres, is the cross-bar of rugby posts?

5. IN which sport might you encounter a hog's back and a white gate?

6. WHAT is the width, in feet, of an American Football pitch?

7. HOW many players are in a Gaelic football team?

8. A WATER polo game consists of four periods of how long?

9. WHICH player wears a C on his jersey in ice hockey?

10. WHAT is the minimum age of a horse in National Hunt racing?

ANSWERS: Turn to page 159

Water Lot of Trivia

1. IN which famous sporting event do competitors strive to win the Diamond Sculls?

2. WHAT is the most popular indoor sport in Britain?

3. WHO received a series of perfect marks for diving at the 1982 World Championships?

4. WHO won an Olympic gold medal for rowing in 1980 and later became an MP?

5. ANOTHER politician captained Britain's Admirals Cup yachting team in 1971? Who?

6. HOW did Bruce Philp make University Boat Race history in 1985?

7. AFTER the United States, which country has won the most Olympic medals for diving?

8. IN which year was canoeing first introduced into the Olympics?

9. WHICH American swimmer won four golds and one silver at the 1976 Olympics in Montreal?

10. WHICH British woman won silver in the women's 400 metres individual medley at the 1980 Olympics in Moscow?

ANSWERS: Turn to page 159

ANSWERS

After Eights

ANSWERS

1. Sergeant Murphy;
2. Mike McCallum;
3. Jana Novotna;
4. Brazilian;
5. Four;
6. Glasgow;
7. The Clown Prince;
8. Lord Killanin;
9. Juan Antonio Samaranch;
10. Brian London.

Athletics

1. Werner Schildhauer;
2. Joan Benoit (USA);
3. Linsey Macdonald;
4. Burglinde Pollak;
5. Tatyana Kanankina;
6. Venanzio Ortis (Italy);
7. John Walker;
8. Jim Hines;
9. Ruth Fuchs;
10. Bruce Jenner.

Lucky Dip

1. 4x400 metres men's relay in which Brian Whittle lost a shoe;
2. A Formula One race;
3. The Marquis of Queensberry;
4. Baseball, fireman is a relief pitcher;
5. 23;
6. Water-skiing;
7. Oxford and Cambridge University at rugby union;
8. Synchronised swimming;
9. The Grand National, winners in 1966, 1949 and 1895;
10. Polo.

Rules & Regulations (2)

ANSWERS

1.   No;
2.   Two years;
3.   The hurley;
4.   Three metres;
5.   Show jumping;
6.   160 feet;
7.   15;
8.   Seven minutes;
9.   Captain;
10.   Three years.

Water Lot of Trivia

ANSWERS

1.   Henley Royal Regatta;
2.   Swimming;
3.   Greg Louganis;
4.   Colin Moynihan;
5.   Edward Heath;
6.   He was the first to row for
       both Oxford & Cambridge;
7.   Sweden;
8.   1936;
9.   John Naber;
10.   Sharon Davies.

Books available from our collection:

You are my Larsson: The Henrik Larsson Story	£5.95
The Martin O'Neill Story	£5.95
The 2002 Prize Crossword Book	£4.99
The Billy Sloan Rock and Pop Quiz Book	£4.99
The Jim Traynor/Hugh Keevins Sports Quiz Book	£4.99
The Joe Punter Racing Guide	£4.99
The Tam Cowan Joke Book	£4.99
VIDEO: Lubo – A Gift From God	£14.99

All these books are available at your local bookshop or newsagent, or can be ordered direct from the publisher. Indicate the number of copies required and fill in the form below.

Send to: *First Press Publishing,*
Daily Record and Sunday Mail,
1 Central Quay,
Glasgow, G3 8DA

or phone: **0141 309 1425** quoting title, author and credit or debit card number.

or fax: **0141 309 3304**, quoting title, author and credit or debit card number.

or email: **orders@first-press.co.uk**

Enclose a remittance* to the value of the cover price plus 75p per book for postage and packing. European customers allow £1.50 per book for post and packing.

* Payment may be made in sterling by UK personal cheque, Eurocheque, postal order, sterling draft or international money order, made payable to First Press Publishing.

Alternatively by Visa/Mastercard/Debit Card Card No.

Expiry Date ☐☐ ☐☐   Valid From Date ☐☐ ☐☐   Issue Number ☐

Signature: _____

Applicable only in the UK and BFPO addresses.

While every effort is made to keep prices low, it is sometimes necessary to increase prices at short notice. First Press Publishing reserve the right to show on covers and charges new retail prices which may differ from those advertised in the text or elsewhere.

NAME AND ADDRESS (IN BLOCK CAPITALS PLEASE)

Name _____

Address _____

_____

_____Postcode_____

First Press will use your information for administration and analysis. We may share it with carefully selected third parties. We, or they, may send you details of goods and services. The information may be provided by letter, telephone or other means. If you do not want your details to be shared please tick this box. ☐